MORE BACK PAGE

BY JACK DOUGLAS MITCHELL

A COLLECTION OF STORIES

FROM THE AMERICAN HUNTER MAGAZINE

ILLUSTRATIONS BY HARRY LLOYD JAECKS

BOOK SERVICE

Copyright © by the National Rifle Association of America

All rights reserved including the right to reproduce
this book or portions thereof.
For information, address the National Rifle Association,
1600 Rhode Island Avenue, N.W., Washington, D.C. 20036

ISBN 0-935998-59-4
Library of Congress Catalog Card Number 89-060501
Printed in the United States
Published 1990

Jacket cover painting (Old Store) by Tom Beecham provided
through the courtesy of Calendar Promotions, Inc.,
Washington, Iowa from the Remington Wildlife Collection.

Published by the
National Rifle Association of America
1600 Rhode Island Avenue, N.W.
Washington, D.C. 20036

George Martin, Executive Director, NRA Publications
Frank A. Engelhardt, Dep. Director & Book Service Manager
Michael A. Fay, Manufacturing Director
Harry L. Jaecks, Art Director

DEDICATION

To my wife, Ruby, for all the years of patient—up to a point—loving tolerance necessary to put up with a hunting-fishing husband . . . *and* his friends.

THE DRAWINGS

As in Jack Mitchell's first book, THE BACK PAGE, Harry Jaecks' exceptional talent captures the warmth, vibrancy and nostalgia of Jack's stories in this latest release, MORE BACK PAGE. Harry's uniquely styled pencil drawings of wildlife and hunting vividly depict those holiday memories, the open meadows and hunting in the woods.

Harry Jaecks is currently the Art Director for NRA Publications. His drawings and watercolors appear regularly in AMERICAN HUNTER and AMERICAN RIFLEMAN magazines. He studied drawing and printmaking at the Maryland Institute of Art and he is a member of the Baltimore Color Society and Ducks Unlimited.

During his free time, Harry paints and exhibits his work at the Chesapeake Bay Foundation Invitational Show, the Easton Waterfowl Festival and New Jersey's Wings and Water, in addition to numerous galleries and juried shows. In 1985, Harry and his wife, artist Jean Brinton Jaecks, were commissioned by the Colonial Williamsburg Foundation to paint a series of eight watercolors for the official Colonial Williamsburg Christmas cards.

Harry's favorite subjects include landscape and wildlife of his native Chesapeake Bay region, as well as rural New England and Pennsylvania.

CONTENTS

To Mary & Earl / Christmas '86   Harry Lloyd Gaede

INTRODUCTION

February 8, 1987,
Mr. George Martin, NRA Publications
Dear George:
   I think it's about time we brought out another book of
Back Page.   Sincerely, Jack

April 21, 1987
Mr. Jack Mitchell, Buxton, N.C.
Dear Jack:
   Why?   Regards, George

April 25, 1987
Mr. Frank Engelhardt, NRA Publications.
Dear Frank:
   I think it's about time we brought out another book of
Back Page.   Siincerely, Jack

July 15, 1987
Mr. Jack Mitchell
Dear Jack:
   Why?   Sincerely, Frank

July 18, 1987
Mr. Tom Fulgham, Editor, AMERICAN HUNTER Magazine
Dear Tom:
I think it's about time we brought out another book of
Back Page.   Sincerely, Jack

November 11, 1987
Mr. Jack Mitchell
Dear Jack:
   Have you mentioned why to George or Frank?
                                    Regards, Tom

November 14, 1987
Mr. George Martin
Dear George:
   Now look, I've conducted extensive sales and market
research on the first book of Back Page and both people
say . . . (on and on and on).
                                    Sincerely, Jack

March 21, 1988
Mr. Jack Mitchell
Dear Jack:
   Frank will do a pro forma and let you know:
                                    Regards, George

March 23, 1988
Mr. Frank Engelhardt
Dear Frank:
   Now look, I've conducted extensive . . . (on and on
and on).   Sincerely, Jack
P.S. Pro what?

May 5, 1988
Memo To Frank, From George:
   What were total sales figures and net return on the Back
Page book?

May 6, 1988
Memo To George, From Frank:
   Umumumumumum.

July 29, 1988
Mr. Jack Mitchell
Dear Jack:
   Frank's sales analysis plus a cross balance comparison
with U.S. Dept. of Commerce report of demographic and
geographic purchase trends 1948 thru 1992 (projected) will
take some study. We will let you know.
                                    Regards, George

September 10, 1988
Memo To George, From Frank:
   Are we going to schedule another Back Page?

November 23, 1988
Memo To Frank, From George:
   Umumumumumum. What are Tom's feelings?

December 19, 1988
Memo To Tom, From Frank:
   Give me your thoughts on another Back Page book.

January 9, 1989
Memo to Frank, From Tom:
   Umumumumumum.

March 5, 1989
Mr. Frank Engelhardt
Dear Frank:
   Now look, you guys, I'm not D. W. Griffith and we are
not exactly birthing a nation. If you will just . . . (on and
on and on).   Sincerely, Jack

January 8, 1990
Mr. Jack Mitchell
Dear Jack:
   Gosh, Jack, in the rush we forgot to let you know. The
book is scheduled for early 1990 publication, titled More Back
Page, and you are far behind deadline. Within 48 hours we
must have from you . . . (on and on and on).
                         Regards, Frank

January 12, 1990
Mr. Frank Engelhardt
Dear Frank:
   Umumumumum.   Sincerely, Jack

Garry Lloyd Jaeder

1 HOW GRANDPA'S DOUBLE GUN SAVED CHRISTMAS

YOUNG Tom Lawson, usually an optimistic 12 year old, had finally come to the conclusion that it wasn't going to be much of a Christmas in their cabin on Pine Lake. There had been no word in more than a month from his dad, who had gone north with their neighbor, Ted Colburn, to trap after the sawmill in town closed down and they were both out of work. Daily trips into town by his mother, Clara, and five year old sister, Laura, to visit the post office hoping for a letter used up a lot of gas in the old truck, but they had no other choice. And Tom always knew there was no letter when his mother came out of the post office with a forced smile for her kids and an armful of catalogs.

Clara Lawson was "on every catalog mailing list in North America," her husband, Bill, used to say. She loved catalogs, and almost every night they sat under the glow of the big Coleman lamp on the kitchen table, Clara poring over her "wish books," Tom doing his homework, and Laura playing with her one and only doll, Alice Elizabeth.

On those dark and stormy nights, when the wind off the lake rattled the windows and whined in the tops of the pines, the little cabin seemed more empty than usual without Bill. Then Clara turned the radio up high, popped corn in the big frying pan on the wood stove, and played "the catalog game" with the kids. Clara would officially issue a $20 credit to both Tom and Laura, which they were free to "spend" on items from the catalogs spread over the table. The trick was to come out *exactly* to $20—no more, no less— for the entire order. Unless you could do that, your "imaginary order" was null and void.

1

Tom got to be quite an expert on handling and shipping fees and postal zones, while his arithmetic steadily improved. His choices ran strongly to hunting knives, minnow traps, hip boots, and a half-dozen snelled fish hooks to "come out even," plus an everlasting search for a .22 caliber rifle. Once he found a special sale on a single-shot .22, but no matter how he figured, it added up to $20.25. He finally had to give it up and turn to other imaginary items.

With Tom's help, little Laura turned immediately to the doll section because, she said, "Alice Elizabeth gets awful lonesome sometimes." But no matter how often Tom and her mother explained to her that it was only a game of "make believe," her big blue eyes filled with tears when her "sealed and ready to go" doll order went not to the post office but back on the shelf . . . with all the other catalog orders.

Tom missed his dad, but he also missed Sal, the half Lab, half German shepherd who had gone north with Bill and Ted as their companion and official guard. Raised with Tom, Sal had proved to be a faultless retriever with the nose of a bloodhound, and when necessary, to have the fierce courage of her wolf-shepherd blood. But with the children she was as gentle as a nurse and just as protective. The day Ted Colburn's truck was loaded to go with their canoe and camping and trapping gear, Clara took Sal by the ears and said softly, "Now you take care of everybody, Sal, and bring them home safe." Tom was on the brink of crying because he so wanted to go along, but when his dad said, "Okay, son, you're the man in charge now," he blinked back his tears.

The weeks dragged by in the little cabin with no word from the north, and Christmas was soon to arrive. Clara had made up her mind to make a big fuss about the holiday—as though Bill was there to share it. Tom cut a little tree near the house, and it stood ready to decorate on Christmas Eve. Clara stayed up long after the children had gone to bed and worked, with tired eyes, on a complete new set of doll clothes for Alice Elizabeth. Fortunately there had been a sale on hunting knives at the store in town, and Tom's gift was already wrapped.

And then just before Christmas the weather turned around. The wind went south, and an unusual December thaw opened up the sloughs and ponds in the big marsh near the cabin. Late that night Tom woke from his bunk bed to hear the loud cries of a huge flock of Canada geese on the wing. He ran to the cabin door in his bare feet and out into the yard, where he looked up into a thick fog that hung treetop high over the woods. Then he heard the geese again in the confusing fog, calling and circling. Swinging over the marsh they were looking for a place to land. Then the calling suddenly ceased with only a few, high-pitched yelps, and Tom knew they had landed in the marsh.

Early the next morning Tom started on his mother about granddad's old, double-barreled goose gun, well oiled and waiting in its full-length case way back in the corner of the loft. "There's geese in the marsh, Mom," Tom pleaded. "I'll get us one for Christmas dinner."

"No, sir, young man. It's too heavy a shotgun for you to handle. Without your father here I wouldn't think of it."

But Tom's mother did think of it as compared to the two jars of canned venison she had planned for Christmas. The prospective sight and smell of a fat wild goose roasting in the oven, basted with the jar of wild grape jelly she'd been saving, finally won out. "Promise me you'll be careful like your father taught you," Clara said softly, and Tom was up the ladder to the loft in a flash.

With trembling hands he pulled the old 12-gauge Parker double—the pride of the family—out of the case, and it shone in oily splendor from the light of the single loft widow. Opening it carefully with the top lever well over like his dad had said, Tom checked the three-inch chambers and looked down the glistening bore of the 30-inch barrels. Closing it with the lever well over and without a snap, Tom put it to his shoulder. It was heavy, all right, but he could point and swing it. In the leather shell box he found six old Remington "Arrow Express" three-inch, No. 2 shot, green paper shells, and their shiny lacquered cases and card-top wad promised power—and recoil. He remembered his dad saying, "This here gun kicks just as hard on one end as it does on the other!"

Well before dawn the next morning, Tom was walking down the road that ran across the marsh with granddad's gun perched confidently on his shoulder. Then he waded across to the old blind he had helped his dad build. The wind came up with the sun and Tom's stomach growled; he hadn't stopped for breakfast, fearing that his mother might change her mind.

3

With both barrels loaded, Tom waited and listened for geese. But no Canadas in sight or earshot for the next long hour. His spirits lagged a bit and he missed Sal, ears up, beside him in the blind. Then they were suddenly there, a small silent flock—right over him! Tom rose up, wobbled a bit, fired the first barrel, and missed. The recoil put him back on his heels, but he recovered enough to get his head down, swing up and with the flaring bird, and fire. The bird faltered, began a long glide, and finally crumpled up in the tall grass along the road.

Tom, his heart pounding, pulled up his boots and reloaded the big gun. As he was about to leave the blind, he saw a familiar shape run down off the high-banked road and go splashing after his goose. It was Sal! Then he saw the truck on the road. It was them! And when Sal showed up with the big goose it was too much for Tom. He tried to wave and shout but ended up in small boy tears. The rest was only a haze to Tom. All at once he was in the truck, hugged by his dad and Ted and trying to hug Sal at the same time. Sal finally dropped the goose, wiggled a bit, and gave him a big, wet kiss.

Then they were home to warm and tearful welcomes from Clara and Laura and with a story about an early freeze up on the river. They had become marooned up north until a plane picked them up, even had a close call with a marauding black bear until Sal ran it off. But a good catch of furs meant presents under the Christmas tree. One long box looked a lot like a .22 rifle, and a doll box was hidden in the loft for Santa to bring. The Christmas dinner of wild goose and wild grape jelly was a happy one, with dad thanking the good Lord and praising a smiling Tom as the mighty hunter and family provider while granddad's goose gun—newly oiled—stood quietly in the corner.

Later that night little Laura came into the room with her new doll, Jennifer, and newly dressed Alice Elizabeth, and said, smiling and looking down at the two dolls in her arms, "You know what? They like each other."

It was then that Tom ran to the cabin door, swung it open and shouted up into the brilliant starlit night, "Merry Christmas, everyone!"

2 THE DOG THAT ATE EVERYTHING

"**D**ON'T worry about these two pointers, Clyde. Best blood and field-trial breeding in the South. Right out of Muscle Shoals Jake. You'll see some real speed and hard points."

"That's just it, John. South Dakota pheasants don't know much about being pointed. They're runners and rarely hold for a dog—not even the best of 'em like these two," my dad said, admiring the two big pointers, King and Flash, in their special dog trailer hauled by our two guests all the way from Dallas to our hunting club near Waubay in the fall of 1937.

"Well, Bill and I have to admit that these long-tailed roosters are new to us and our dogs. But they're game *birds*, and these are *bird* dogs. Don't worry, they'll point 'em."

Well, they pointed 'em all right. Immediately. No sooner had the dogs hit the ground on the edge of the weed-filled ditch bordering the big cornfield than they both froze on hard points. This ditch was evidently full of bird scent, but the pheasants had disappeared in the tall weeds, running like rabbits—heads and tails out flat—down the ditch. John and Bill looked at each other in silent amazement.

Dad soon had our forces organized to drive the cornfield. Three blockers on the end and seven drivers, including our two guests and dogs, to walk the rows of standing corn. A good "dirty" cornfield—full of weeds. It was on the edge of dust-bowl country, and the drought-stricken farmers did little cultivating.

Dad blew his whistle, and we started the drive. We had gone only a few yards down the rows when both King and Flash went on point. Beautiful, high-tailed style. When we stopped, birds began getting up all around us. To their credit, the two pointers were steady as a rock—in the best field trial style—to shot and wing until a big rooster stopped in midair and dropped with a solid "thump," barely missing King on

5

point, as another pheasant raced right under Flash's nose.

Well, that did it. Both dogs broke point and began chasing the birds up and across the rows of standing corn. John was right. They had *speed,* all right. And more cackling pheasants filled the air with the roar of wings.

And then the final blow to the "pride of Muscle Shoals" came as the excited dogs began giving tongue like a pair of Walker hounds hot on the track. Hundreds of pheasants boiled up out of that cornfield. Roosters and hens, flying and gliding in all directions, lit running on the far-off prairie and quickly disappeared.

During all this commotion, both John and Bill were blasting on their dog whistles like angry traffic cops at busy intersections. But to no avail. They kept blowing until exhausted, then stood there in the "empty" cornfield, red faced, panting, and looking at each other until John started to laugh. And somehow we all laughed with him as Bill said, "Did you ever see such *speed*?"

Muscle Shoals Jake, the great pointer from Alabama, was a national field-trial champion. An active producer at stud, many were his descendants, and we got to know one of these dogs very, very well. His kennel name was Bim. Dad bought him as a finished Georgia quail dog in 1936. A pleasure to watch, he was a big-going, horizon-hunting, quail machine.

I can see him now, black head fading off into a mixture of tan and gray. I think they called his type "Rip Rap" in Georgia. And if a dog can have a cheerful, friendly, smiling face, Bim had one. But beneath that happy and innocent look lurked a hardheaded, willful, bird-finding devil with the all-consuming, savage appetite of a Serengeti hyena. Bim ate anything that didn't eat him first and then, between burps, pleasantly smiled up at you.

Dad once sent me a letter from Atlanta recounting in detail the first day they hunted Bim on a quail lease they had just acquired.

Dad wrote: "We followed the dogs in the wagon up to the edge of a cotton field where a farmer's small house sat out in the middle of a clearing. Bim, busily hunting quail with the other dog, suddenly stopped stock-still, raised his head, and sniffed the air. With that, he made a beeline for the house, ran up onto the porch, disappeared through the back door, and—believe it or not—raced out the front door with a big ham bone in his mouth followed by the whole family—

8

the farmer, his wife, and kids yelling and throwing pots and pans at the dog that had snatched their midday dinner right off the kitchen table. We never saw the ham bone again (he probably swallowed it whole), and it took Lon Davis (a native Georgian and Dad's hunting partner) quite a while to quiet them all down with a $5 bill and a box of shotgun shells. After the family returned to the house, Bim suddenly showed up in front of the mule-drawn wagon and locked on a hard point—biggest covey of the day."

After our hunting move to South Dakota from Georgia, Bim, appetite and all, soon joined us. Although he proved to be a star performer on Hungarian partridge, he not only pointed them, he occasionally ate one—just to keep up his strength, I suppose.

One day, I caught him swallowing a downed partridge—feathers, legs, and all—in what seemed a single gulp. Yelling, "No, no," I grabbed him by the collar, "whupped" him hard, and shook him till he rattled. He accepted all this without a whimper or yelp and immediately went back to hunting. Within minutes, he located another covey.

My brother Bob and I put down two Huns on the rise, and another hard-hit one sailed over a hill with Bim in hot pursuit. Following him closely, I arrived just in time to see him busily digging a hole to bury the bird. He ducked away from my angry yells and swinging cap and ran off about 50 feet, sat down, and gave me his quizzical, almost innocent look as if to say, "What's all the fuss about? I wasn't *eating* the bird." Mad as I was, I almost had to smile. And then Bob spoiled it all by laughing.

I guess what really got to me with Bim was his habit of trying to crawl up into my lap at the end of the day when we were sitting around the clubhouse stove. He couldn't quite make it and usually left one hind leg on the floor. In spite of a hard day of pretty unsuccessful dog discipline, he wanted to be friends. Even after the day he ate the insides out of five pheasants hung up in the back of the station wagon and then smiled up at me in complete innocence with the feathers still sticking to his lips. And I gave it to him hard that day.

So long ago. Yet there are times when I wish he were back– half in my lap– so I could reach up and scratch behind his briar-torn, leathery ears and hear his sigh of content. All is forgiven, Bim, you old rascal. Wherever you are, all is forgiven. 9

I NEVER ASKED HER 3

HAVE you ever noticed that the wives of outdoor writers are usually cast as antagonists? Friendly and, no doubt, loving, but somehow the wives are always loudly on the side of common sense when it comes to the unreasonable number of guns and fishing rods their husbands own, plus the too many days they spend hunting and fishing. Many funny stories have been told about this traditional conflict and how to outwit the female competition and still keep peace in the family. Evidently it's the standard situation. Knowing all that, you can imagine how surprised I was recently to realize that my wife, Ruby, didn't fit into that category at all. I'll probably have to turn in my outdoor writer's membership card, but here goes.

Last spring, I was sitting on a lonely beach on North Carolina's Outer Banks, soaking a big chunk of cut mullet in the Atlantic Ocean in hopes that a stray channnel bass would swim by and give my bait a look. Bunches of white-winged scoters were moving along the shore against a northeast wind. Just beyond the breakers these big, chunky sea ducks were getting my full attention when I realized that I had been joined by a young man, another hopeful angler. We exchanged greetings and commiserated on the lack of fish while I watched him make his cast, set his rod in a sand spike, and settle down near me.

We were soon lost in the pleasant and almost hypnotic trance that eventually seizes all beach fishermen—staring out over the blue and boundless ocean, listening to the rumbling and grumbling of the surf. Every once in a while the scoters flew by, and we began to talk about how they were hunted. I told him about places like Cape Cod, where a line of anchored dories holds crouching gunners waiting for the scoters to run the gauntlet, and how the hunters sometimes use huge, oversize decoys at the end of the line to attract attention to the floating racks of silhouette coot decoys. Shooting from a pitching dory on a choppy sea, hunters wait for the skunkheads, whitewings and black coots to loom up out of the fog. It's a wild scene.

"Man, I'd like to try that," he said. "And maybe I can now since things have changed with me."

"How's that?" I inquired.

"She left me. My wife did. Told me it was either her or my hunting and fishing." And then, turning to me with sad indignation, he asked, "What the heck kind of a choice is that?"

I was about to say it was up to him when I heard my wife calling to me from the top of the sand dunes behind us. She told me that she was going into town and that my lunch was on the kitchen table.

"Thanks," I said, and we waved at each other.

After a while the young man asked, "How does *your* wife feel about all your hunting and fishing?"

At that moment I thought I felt a tug on my line, and as I was reeling in to check the bait, I considered the question. Finally I said, "I really don't know, I never asked her." And somehow I never had. I had never asked her how she felt about my not always being home on her birthday, October 18, an immutable date that often coincided with the opening day of the upland game hunting season. I once considered writing the fish and game commission about this problem, but never got around to it.

I had never asked her about all those good breakfasts for hunters and for dogs that she prepared before dawn on duck hunting days, and the neatly packed lunch, thermos, and package of dog biscuits waiting at the front door with all my other duffle. Come to think of it, no matter what ungodly hour I left home to hunt or to catch the tide, I never left a silent or unlit house. Of course, there were admonitions at the door about watching the weather, and an occasional, "Give my best to those other idiots and tell them I think you all are completely mad"—but always a "good luck," a pat for the eager dogs, a quick kiss for me, and a smile, often with a yawn. No, I never asked my wife how she felt about it. It just happened.

And then the return of the mighty hunter, often after dark, to a warm kitchen and a hot meal—maybe a little dried out, but still hot. If I was much later than expected, the ever-

11

present orders not to track up the kitchen and to take off "all those horrible muddy things" in the garage or the mudroom might be a little sharper than usual, but she was always there. Somehow, the dogs were not subject to these same house rules under such circumstances and were welcomed, muddy paws and all, into the kitchen. In fact, she often interrupted my story of the hunt and my amazing exploits with, "That's all fine, but did the dogs have a good time?"

"Oh, for the love of Mike, why don't you ask them?" I'd ask with a sigh. So she would ask the dogs, and they would wag their tails and grin an answer.

"Yes, they had a good time," I would say.

"That's nice," she'd say, and that's how we—the dogs and I—were welcomed home.

In fact, if it hadn't been for the dogs, I doubt that Ruby would have been so understanding about hunting. I well remember our first bird dog, a springer spaniel pup named Henry. Not a usual name for a dog, but he was born on the Fourth of July, and since Patrick Henry is identified with that date, my wife called the puppy Henry (which gives you some idea of how my wife sees things). Long before we had any children, Henry was the center of our family. The first game he flushed as a four-month-old puppy was a pair of mallards from a roadside ditch with Ruby as a reluctant observer. As luck would have it, I made a clean double, and Henry promptly half dragged both birds, one at a time, to Ruby. She clapped her hands with delight and said, "Do it again, so he can retrieve some more!" She had joined the team.

I am now moved to inquire if any of you mature readers remember an old movie called *Viva Zapata*, starring Marlon Brando as the revolutionary Mexican general. Brando, in full dress uniform, called on his fiancé, the daughter of the mayor. Sitting stiffly on a chair in the formal parlor, he exchanges proverbs with the two *dueñas* (chaperones), waving their fans in the summer heat. They compliment the general on his uniform, and he counters with, "It is said that a monkey in a silk suit is still a monkey." The *dueñas* titter politely and keep on fanning. Then a *dueña* congratulates the general on his forthcoming marriage, and the general replies, unforgettably, "It is said that he who has a good wife wears heaven in his hat."

I don't know whether or not my wife ever saw this movie. I never asked her.

4 WILD GOOSE JACKSON

THERE was no question about it. Bill Jackson was a fullfledged go-getter. When you first met him, it didn't take long to feel the impact of his competitive spirit. Whatever the contest, Bill was out to win. He liked to say, "Show me a good loser, and I'll show you a loser." And the old quotation, "It's not whether you win or lose, it's how you play the game," brought only a snort of contempt and a shake of the head from Bill.

Folks in our town weren't familiar with the proper psychological terms to explain Bill's actions, but we sort of figured that he was compensating for a pretty rough childhood when winning at anything was a rare occurrence. Some of us remembered the Jacksons and all the raggedy kids that seemed to spill out of the old, ramshackle, unpainted house with the sagging porch on the edge of town. Bill Jackson, a happy-go-lucky guy, was a part-time logger and a full-time poacher who regularly roamed the woods with rifle and shotgun.

Both of Bill's parents died when he was young, and his brothers and sisters eventually left home. All except Bill, who was a good enough student to win a scholarship and work his way through college where he was a football star—an all-conference halfback. Coming back to his hometown, he became one of our first real estate men, and his hard work and aggressiveness helped him prosper as the county changed from logging to small industry and tourism. Bill carried the ball hard every day.

The years rolled on. Bill married Jean Peterson, and they had a son. According to what Jean told my wife, from the

13

first time little Jim reached up from his crib to grasp his father's finger with his warm, tiny hand, Bill was a goner. It usually happens to all fathers, but Bill was now more than ever determined to make Jim, his only child, a winner.

I can remember little Jim toddling after a football on the lawn long before he was big enough to pick it up and trying his best on his short, fat legs to keep up with his daddy as they ran wind sprints around the outside of the house.

With his dad's constant coaching, Jim became a good, all-around young athlete. But about the time he went to high school, he began to rebel. Something in his blood began to turn him to the beckoning hills around the town. All it took was for him to find his grandfather's old single-shot .22 rifle in the attic, and Jim became a hunter—walking the same mountain trails as his grandfather had.

Even as a freshman Jim made the high school football team, and although he would rather have spent his Saturdays in the hills, he was a good, steady halfback, much to the delight and pride of his father. All went well until the big game with Boonesville High, an ancient rival. It was the last quarter when Boonesville tied the score. On the following kickoff, the ball went tumbling through the air straight downfield to Jim Jackson. All eyes were on the ball—all except those of Jim, who was looking straight up as a big flock of Canada geese suddenly swung out of a fleecy-white cloud high over his head. The ball bounced off Jim's shoulder, and in the scramble, Boonesville unfortunately recovered. Two plays later and in spite of two fierce defensive tackles by Jim, they scored, and the game was over.

In the heat of the town's defeat, you can imagine how everyone yelled at Jim. And all he did was look sadly at them and say, "I'm sorry, but it was the first flock of Canada geese I'd seen this year, and I just had to know where they were going." Later on, I heard that Bill left the field alone and refused to talk to Jim for days. And then to make things worse, everyone at school and some of the crueler townsmen began to call Jim "Wild Goose Jackson." But Jim had the courage to grin back at them and say, "Aw, come on now. It's only a game." And then, just to prove it, he scored the winning touchdown the following Saturday at Mountville.

I guess everyone in town finally forgave Jim, all except Bill, who still felt betrayed and couldn't quite understand his son's attitude. And then, to make it worse, Jim began to spend his evenings helping Art Chase teach the survival course and the hunter safety classes held at the high school. "Just a lot of nonsense," Bill complained. "And there's no money in it, either. I gave up hunting years ago. A waste of time. There's nothing there to win. No competition in hunting." And then when he heard that Jim wanted to study forestry in college instead of business administration, the breach really widened. It was beginning to look as though Bill and Jim were really going to lose each other in the father's failure to understand or even respect the values of his son.

Then came the blizzard that locked our town in an icy grip for 48 hours. I was traveling the entire state in those days, but I was working the southern tier of counties and missed the big storm. I got back in town late one night, and the next morning I stopped at the Busy Bee Cafe for a cup of coffee. This is where I heard about Bill and Jim in the blizzard.

According to what I could gather, Bill had somehow become involved in a crazy bet here at the Busy Bee with his business rival, Glenn Morgan, who claimed Bill was against hunting because he couldn't get a buck of his own. Bill bet Glenn $50 that he could. So Bill and Jim left to hunt Bear Mountain the day it started to blow, and they got snowed in right below Collins Ridge. Jean was worried sick, but all the roads were blocked, and there was nothing to do but wait. Art Chase said he'd bet they were all right because Jim had his survival day pack and knew what to do. And sure enough, they showed up about noon on the third day, hungry and pretty exhausted, but okay—and friends again, Jean put them both to bed.

It seems that Jim knew how to burrow under a shelf of rocks, build a fire to warm the cave, prepare some freeze-dried grub, and wrap the space blanket around them as they waited out the storm. They had plenty of time to talk, and both of them came back smiling.

Now it was time for Bill Jackson to show up at the Busy Bee to pay off his bet.

"Behold, the mighty hunter," Glenn Morgan said with a grin. "What did you get?"

"Never even saw a deer. Here's your money," Bill said. "But I'll tell you what I did get."

"What's that?" Glenn asked.

And I sort of choked on my coffee when I heard Bill say quietly, "I got back my son."

15

5 A GROCERY LIST FROM GOOSE ANKLE, TEXAS

MAN! How did it get this cold? Think I'll just move around to the other side of this tree and get out of the wind. But then I won't be able to see down the valley and keep my eye on that runway where a big buck could show up any minute now.

"Any minute," my brother Bob said when he put me on this stand what seems like two weeks ago. "Keep alert now and don't move around too much." Lord knows I've got on enough clothes and almost solid blaze orange, too. While I was puffing my way up here, Bob turned to me and said with a grin, "You look like a barrel on fire." Still the same smart-aleck kid brother, but he does know this country.

Better check that safety again. Click "off," click "on." Open the bolt. Okay, lock it up. Click "off," click "on." Hey, I've got to remember to tell the gang tonight about my Uncle Bill Wolf from Rockfield, Wisconsin, and the time he borrowed that old Remington Model 8 autoloader from my dad—the one with the big side-lever safety.

As Uncle Bill told it, "First, I oiled up everything on that rifle good and sighted her in. Went way up in Vilas County. Never saw a horn until the third day when the weather changed and it went down to about zero. Just going along slow that morning and here he comes. Absolutely the biggest buck I'd ever seen. So I stopped dead still, slid off my mitt, and went to ease off that safety so it wouldn't click. The buck was still coming right at me. And then—wouldn't you know— the safety was stuck. So I slowly increased the pressure, still keeping my eye on that big buck, who by now wasn't more than 50 yards away. He kept on coming, and I kept on pressing. Then he stopped and just looked at me like he was sort of bored. That safety wouldn't budge, so I finally kneeled down, put the rifle on my knee, and pushed the lever with both thumbs.

"It was probably just my frustration, but I swear I saw that buck actually lean up against a tree, cross his front legs, and yawn. With all that oil, the safety was frozen to the receiver. I finally stood up and banged the lever on a tree. The buck turned and strolled slowly into the brush. And I never saw another buck the rest of the trip." Moral: Don't oil your rifle in zero-degree weather. Use a squirt of powdered graphite.

Now the cold seems to be settling in around the small of my back—the lumbar region. Lumbar. Strange name. Like lumber. Maybe that's why they say your back is stiff as a board. Enough of that, now. Keep alert. Look around. Check that runway again.

If I had known it was going to be this cold, I would have wrapped a layer of newspaper around my middle—between my long underwear and my wool shirt. Nothing like it to keep you warm, even if you do crackle a bit when you walk. And if you get too warm, you can always reach in and unwrap yourself.

I remember way back when Bob had just discovered this part of the country and insisted I join him on a hunt. Full of big bucks, he said. It was almost as cold then as it is now. The wind came from the south on the second day, and it started to warm up. So there I was, climbing up this ridge, wrapped up in the Sunday supplement. When I got up to the stand Bob had carefully directed me to, I was giving off so much steam that I dug around under my shirt and pulled out my newspaper insulation. Now this was done to cool off, not to get something to read. But I must admit I am a compulsive reader and not at all selective. In fact, my dear mother used to laugh at me reading the newspaper, in which she wrapped the garbage, on my way to the trash can.

I once heard an old Montana cowpuncher tell how he used to sit around the camp fire after a lonely supper out on the range and read the labels on the tin cans—just for something to read. Speaking of cowpunchers, I wonder if that story is true about the old cowboy who was told he looked just like the Marlboro man in the cigarette ads. "Didn't mind that much," he said, "until I saw one of those ads. The cowboy had his spurs on upside down."

Keep alert. Better take another look down the valley and stop my mind from wandering into the past. Okay, okay. Nothing there yet. Now back to that Sunday supplement that I had worn up the mountain. It was a full-page feature written by a popular Hearst columnist of those times named Arthur Brisbane. Seems that Mr. Brisbane had figured out that, according to the law of probability, if you put 100 chimpanzees into a room and kept them pecking away at random on 100 typewriters, they would eventually type out *everything* ever written in the English language. Even now the whole concept boggles the mind—especially my mind, which isn't hard to boggle these days.

Imagine being in that room of typewriting monkeys. You could sidle up to a chimp pecking away, look over his hairy shoulder, and watch him beat out the entire First Canto of John Milton's *Paradise Lost*. And across the table, another hard-typing chimp has just knocked out the complete grocery list written by Mrs. Elmer Perkins on August 10, 1897, in the small town of Goose Ankle, Texas. As I was working my way from monkey to monkey down the long tables, a shadow suddenly fell across the paper. There stood brother Bob.

"I thought you were hunting," he said quietly.

"I am," I said.

"Didn't you see that big buck go by?" asked Bob.

"Nope," I said.

"Where did you get the newspaper?" questioned Bob.

"Wore it up here under my shirt like underwear," I answered. "It was too hot, so I took it off." Then Bob sighed, shook his head, and sat down beside me. We both looked down the valley.

Now, my brother and I have always been the best of friends, and there isn't a mean bone in his body. But I did hear later that he said, "I drove this big buck right by him. When I finally got there, he was sitting under a tree *reading* his underwear."

So, like I said, you've got to keep constantly alert on a deer stand. You never know when your brother will sneak up on you.

THE DOG THEY LEFT BEHIND 6

IT was a busy fall day at Charlie's Service Station. Charlie Adams and his helper, Ed Lawton, were on the go from the time they opened up at 6 a.m. until they closed at nine o'clock that night, and it wasn't until about an hour before Charlie locked up that he noticed the old dog watching every car that drove in. As Charlie tells it, "He'd get up from under the tire rack, stand there with his tail wagging hopefully, and then sort of sag and go back to his spot. Guess somebody just went off and left him there. Wasn't that a rotten thing to do?"

In a small town like ours, filling stations don't open until noon on Sunday, and when I pulled into Charlie's about 1 p.m., the old dog was still there under the tire rack, still watching every car expectantly. Charlie had opened a can of dog food for him and had given him a pan of water, but outside of a few laps of water, nothing was touched. He looked like a cross between a black Lab and a German shepherd, a smart-looking old character with some gray in his muzzle. But he had a hurt and puzzled look about him that was hard to take.

"What are you going to do with him, Charlie?" I asked.

"Darned if I know. I don't dare bring home another dog or Mavis will leave me flat. And Ed's wife has a house full of cats. And you know what will happen if I hand him over to the county dog catcher," he sighed. Then he added, "Hey, how about you?"

"I'd be glad to take him, but Doc Miller says Mary's bronchial asthma—or whatever you call it—is aggravated by dog hair in or around the house."

So I left Charlie's place not feeling good about anything at all. The next morning on my way to work, I almost hated to look as I drove by the station, but there he was under the tire rack, watching every car. Although it was really none of my business, I stopped in again at noon on my way home for lunch.

"Well, he ate a little this morning," Charlie said. "But he's still watching every car. Any ideas?"

As we stood there looking at each other, who should drive into the pumps but old Bill Green, wearing his usual scowl. "Mean Bill Green" they called him—but not to his face, I can tell you. Big as a house and strong as an ox, he was somewhat feared and grudgingly respected by almost everyone in town. Usually a silent old sourpuss with an occasional outburst of temper, he seemed mad at the world and just about everybody in it. He lived in a big, old house on the edge of Baxter Marsh and kept pretty much to himself ever since his wife just up and left him years ago—just after he got back from Korea. He did a little trapping, odd jobs, and a lot of duck hunting, but nobody really knew him.

As the old dog came out to check Bill's truck, I noticed that Bill had two nice mallard drakes in the back together with his roll-up duck blind and some decoys. The dog was about to turn around—disappointed one more time—when he stopped short and made two audible sniffs. He had winded the ducks and suddenly rose up with his front paws on the tailgate of the truck and took a look for himself.

"Hey, get out of there," Bill snarled as he climbed out of the truck. The old dog looked at him sadly for a moment, dropped to all fours, and eased slowly back toward the tire rack.

"Where did you get that old mutt?" Bill muttered as Charlie picked up the gas hose.

"Somebody just went off and left him here," Charlie said.

Bill merely grunted. "Do you think he's a retriever?"

"Sure looks like one," Charlie answered. "Why don't you try him?"

"Me? What do I want with an old mutt like that?" Then he looked over at the dog, who was watching them both with his ears up, almost as though he knew what they were talking about.

"How much?" Bill asked.

"Nothing. Whoever he belonged to just went off and left him."

21

After a long pause, Bill said almost too quietly to hear, "Yeah, I know how that is." Then he stepped back from the truck, looked over at the dog, and called in his rough voice, "Hey, boy. Come on, old black dog. Let's see if you can find that mallard I put down this morning."

And then, as though he'd been waiting, the dog got up, trotted over to the truck, and with an almost youthful bounce, jumped up into the back. And off they went to find that mallard.

Going by Charlie's again on my way home that night, I was saddened to see the dog back in his spot under the tire rack. Guess it just hadn't worked out between him and Bill Green. Too bad, I thought.

Early the next morning, I noticed that my left front tire needed some air, so I'm back at Charlie's just in time to see Bill Green drive in, jerk his truck to a halt, and looking madder than ever, head for the office where I could hear him complaining loudly to Charlie.

"Some dog you loaned me yesterday. Found that mallard right off, but when I tried to take him out to the point, he just took off and left me. I've had enough of that kind of treatment. Never mind about his wanting to get back here. He *left* me."

Then I noticed that Bill had dropped a glove on his angry march to the office. I watched the old dog pick it up off the blacktop, walk over to the truck, and wait patiently for Bill. When Bill arrived, there sat the dog, gazing up at him with the glove in his mouth and a pleading look in his eye.

"Now what?" Bill asked. And glowering down at the dog, he snatched the glove out of its mouth, stood there for a long moment, sighed deeply, and said, "Okay. Looks like our luck has *finally* changed." Another long pause, then, "Come on, Lucky, get in the truck. Let's go home."

As Lucky started to walk around to the back, Bill stopped him, opened the cab door, and in one bounce, Lucky was on the front seat. And when Bill got in, Lucky tried to give his new boss a big, wet kiss. Then we saw Bill actually laugh and gently push him away.

So as Charlie and I stood there grinning like a couple of kids, we watched Mean Bill Green and his new dog, Lucky, go down the road.

7 CHRISTMAS EVE ON WHITEFISH CREEK

THE "Mulligan Annual Scent and Lures" calendar nailed to the tar-paper wall of Lonnie Briggs' trapping shack on the banks of Whitefish Creek showed the date December 25 in festive type with a green holly wreath and red bow around it. But it didn't look like much of a Christmas coming up for Lonnie deep in the Canadian wilderness on December 24.

The young trapper had planned to be out of camp with his traps picked up long before now, ready for his annual mid-winter holiday trip down to Longbow at the head of the big lake where he would sell his fur, pick up a few supplies, drink a few beers at the trading post, and maybe get invited to a friend's cabin for Christmas Day. "Batching it," as they called Lonnie's life style, was all right for awhile but this time of year the memories of other Christmases back in Ohio got pretty strong, and he needed people.

And then the weather turned around, starting with only a few casual snowflakes drifting silently down through the jack pines when Lonnie was on the northernmost loop of his trapline. But by the time he had made it back down to Beaver Crossing it was a howling blizzard, with the snowshoe trail lost in the snow. From then on westward to Whitefish Creek it was entirely by compass worn on a rawhide thong around his neck. Cradled from time to time in his snow-covered mitts, the unwavering needle pointed the way as Lonnie turned his back to the icy blast and followed. Miles later, with lungs about to burst and leg muscles knotted, he suddenly snowshoed into the frozen creek and the welcome sight of his shack. He was home.

Soon out of the storm and with aching fingers, he shook a match from the bottle on the shelf, lit it, and touched its flame to pitch pine kindling in the little black stove waiting patiently for him in the cold dark room. The resinous sticks quietly caught fire, and its warm and welcome blaze told Lonnie that he had licked the wilderness once more and

23

made it home one more time. As he pulled off his parka the thong of the compass caught around his ears. He took it off from his neck and sat down heavily with a deep sigh on his pine-bough bunk, and while the roaring, little stove beat back the frostline, he held the cold brass case of the compass in his numb fingers. Little had he known that when Ellen, the girl he left behind in Ohio, gave him the compass as a going-away Christmas gift with a tag that said, "To find your way back to me—and many more Christmases to spend together. Love, Ellen," that so many Christmases would have gone by without the compass needle pointing south to lead his way back home to Ohio.

Lonnie, an orphan, had always been a restless hunter with an unquenchable desire to see what lay over the next ridge of hills. It was this love of the woods, the promise of adventure and an overactive imagination that finally led him to quit school after his first year of college and go north to make his fortune. He probably never admitted that he saw himself returning to the small town of Pottsville, Ohio, laden down with gold dust (and a few nuggets, of course) heavily bearded, wearing beaded moccasins (the gift of an Indian princess), and with exciting tales of glory and adventure in the far north told between thoughtful puffs on a straight-stemmed, black brier pipe . . . just like in the movies.

But, as a lot of us have found out, the movies and real life experience rarely match up—except that you have to pay admission to see both. And Lonnie had paid his admission early in the game. It was a bad case of "gold fever" fed by secret maps, rumors of lost mines, and barroom tales of striking it rich. One long, hot, black, fly-bitten summer, shovelling gravel alone on a nameless wilderness river for a total return of $28.42 (Canadian) cured Lonnie of "gold fever"—permanently.

Ellen's letters had followed him faithfully for awhile, full of eager and tender plans for his return and their future together. But as months grew into years and Lonnie's compass continued to point north over the next mountain, their correspondence cooled, slowed down, and finally stopped.

Lonnie, never a big man, was now a rawboned, tough trapper and hunter who lived by the trap and the rifle. No longer a tenderfoot, he had learned the hard way and, as they say, "he could string steel and read fur sign" with the best of them. Deep inside, however, he still planned as soon as he could make a good stake to go home. But to whom? That was the sad question he carried with him constantly.

As the room warmed and the teakettle began to sing, Lonnie set about preparing this lonely Christmas Eve celebration "dinner for one." Moose was on the menu—again. A 1400-pound bull moose killed in September goes a long, long way. Good, solid, nutritious venison but compared to the glistening, fat and juicy Christmas turkey ("White meat only, please") Lonnie imagined being served back home, it seemed pretty dry and pretty dark. As he put the frozen steaks in the pan he suddenly heard the sound of snowshoes being hung on the outside cabin wall, a loud bang on the door, and in with the blast of the blizzard came big Chris McDonald, an older fellow trapper from up north. Dropping a snow-covered pack the size of a muskrat house on the floor he boomed, "Merry Christmas, you skinny runt. When do we eat?"

"Ye gods! Where'n hell did you come from?" Lonnie sang out happily. "I thought you were Santa Claus."

"So I am, you young woods rat. Can't stand my own company at Christmas. Brought you three spruce hens—I pulled their craw—and your mail from Longbow."

"Mail?" said Lonnie. "Where is it?"

"Keep your shirt on, kid. Mostly catalogs. They want you to buy an electric shoe polisher, I think." And Chris laughed till his belly shook.

As Lonnie pawed through the mailbag full of mail order announcements he finally said quietly, "No letters?"

"Now that you mention it, kid, believe I did have a letter here somewhere," Chris said with a grin. "Kept it up here in my shirt pocket. Female writing, and it smells good, too. Ellen somebody?"

With trembling hands Lonnie took the familiar envelope from Chris, fumbled it open, read it eagerly, and let out a whoop of joy. "She wants me to come home!"

"Well, go home then, you darn fool. Everybody needs somebody," Chris said and produced another present from his giant pack—a flask of single malt Scotch whiskey. "Merry Christmas, kid."

Later that night, as the blizzard began to blow itself out, a lone snowy owl flew across the moon and looked down with cold yellow eyes at the sound of loud, off-key carolling. It was Christmas Eve on the banks of Whitefish Creek.   25

8 ANYBODY ELSE SHOOT?

OVER the thousands of years that man has been hunting, certain inflexible rules have been developed to control the conduct of a hunter who hunts with others. And with that formal opening, let us turn directly to the point of "claiming"—the abhorrent practice of claiming that your shot, and your shot only, downed the game when more than one shooter was involved.

If you remember your history, you're familiar with "Ivan the Terrible" and "Pepin the Short." Now, I want you to meet "Henry the Claimer," an actual character from my checkered past. Henry (that's not his real name) was a good citizen—sober, industrious, and undoubtedly kind to his wife and children. But when it came to hunting, he became an all-out, highly irritating, unreconstructed, compulsive claimer. He was convinced that any bird that came down was his and that the mere coincidence of someone else shooting at the same bird he was merely increased his already awesome skill.

Henry was turning into a problem, and he was often the subject of hushed discussions by his fellow hunters with much head shaking and furtive glances over their shoulders to see if he was around. Henry was on his way to becoming a lone and solitary hunter when a few of his companions who really liked the guy decided to reform him.

Henry was a South Dakota pheasant hunter, and so it was in one of those endless prairie cornfields that his lesson began. In those days, shooting started at noon, the limit was 10 birds a day, and the pheasants were thick in the corn. It was what we called a "dirty" cornfield—full of seeds, weeds, and pheasants. With three blockers on the end and five drivers stationed with Henry in the middle, off they went.

No sooner had they started down the rows when the birds began to get up and the shooting began. Working their devilish plan, the hunters, not waiting for Henry's usual claim, called out, "Good shot, Henry!" every time a bird was downed. They then proceeded to fill Henry's game coat with the big roosters. Overriding his protests, they gave every bird to Henry, slapped him on the back, and loudly complimented his shooting until, with his game coat bulging and wire-loop carriers of pheasants draped around his neck, Henry could barely raise his arms to shoot.

Reaching the end of the field, the blockers called out, "How're you'll doing?"

"Great," they yelled back. "Henry got 'em all!"

When poor Henry and all his pheasants finally staggered out of the corn rows up to the station wagon, he leaned, exhausted, against the tailgate, looked around at his grinning friends, and said, "I think I see what you mean." And so Henry gave up "claiming" and hunted happily ever after.

It was called "Honeysuckle Blind" down in the southwest corner of the field, and the tenacious vines had completely covered the woven-wire fence that hid the long, wooden bench and its row of hunters from the sharp eyes of Canada geese as they flew over. Whoever built the blind there on Remington Farms evidently believed that goose hunters love company because the 12-foot-long bench could seat enough hopeful hunters to form a men's glee club.

But on this particular bright and windy hunting day, Honeysuckle Blind was deserted. The few geese that were moving were going high over the east blinds, and it was a long time between shots. But then the wind hauled, and the straggling flights of big birds began to move to the southwest and drift down over Honeysuckle Blind. One by one (and occasionally two by two), the hunters began to change blinds and saunter casually down to the corner blind. No undue or unsportsmanlike haste, just polite drifting and picking their way carefully along the red, muddy, clay road to the blind. Soon, the long bench was almost filled, and I was there in the middle—in the baritone section. So many shotgun barrels were sticking up out of the vines that, from the front, our blind must have looked like a rustic pipe organ or a blued-steel picket fence.

The occasion was the Annual Gun Writers Seminar held that year at Remington Farms on Maryland's Eastern Shore, where the Remington Arms people presented their new line of products for the coming year. And, of course, we all managed to work in a little goose and duck hunting. As we pushed along on the bench to make room for new arrivals, the last seat went to a well-known publisher and editor in the outdoor writing field. A typically harassed New Yorker with the usual urgent appointments elsewhere, he had, at the last moment, postponed his pressing return to Madison Avenue and joined the hunt without changing into his hunting clothes. It was in the days of pork-pie hats, short car coats, and, of course, low-top shoes. You can imagine how our late-arriving friend looked coming down the muddy road, trying to avoid the puddles and holding his windblown pork-pie hat in one hand and his borrowed shotgun in the other.

He was noisily welcomed with a lot of kidding from the bench, and no sooner had he taken the end seat when a big flock of Canadas showed up on the horizon and began to come our way.

"Mark north," was the cry. "Sit still. Quit waving those gun barrels," was the advice from some of the older hunters. Fighting the strong southwest wind, the flock rose and fell against the blue sky but kept coming our way. They were pretty high but still in range. Now if that wind didn't blow them off course. . . .

Just as they were about to come right over us, a strong gust of wind blew the flock to our right and high above us. At that, the entire bench of shooters rose to their feet and opened fire—all except me, who leaned over and put my hands over my ears. The cannonading of all those full-choke, 12-gauge guns loaded with high-base goose loads was almost deafening, and as the air above us filled with wads and smoke, I looked up to see one lone goose pitch off to the side and go down.

With that, our New York friend shot out of the blind like a trained Labrador and off he went after the goose. We all watched him make the retrieve, splashing over his low shoes in ankle-deep mud. And back he came to the long blind with its row of hunters, holding the big bird by a wing tip in one hand and his shotgun in the other. Standing there before us in his now-muddy city clothes and breathing hard from the retrieve, he said—unforgettably and with a straight face—"Did anybody else shoot?"

29

AN INSIDE OUTDOOR TIP ON SUSPENDER BUTTONS

A N outdoor library today contains a most amazing variety of books dealing with an infinite range of "how to" subjects, all aimed at advising you and me—the trusting, friendly, hunter/fisherman type. From "Little Known Facts About Charging Grizzly Bears" to "Tips On Stalking The Sora Rail" to "A Short History Of The Nail Knot" to "How To Stew Up Your Own Catfish Bait Without Getting Thrown Out Of The House," we are being educated. We are being advised, consoled, encouraged, and stimulated to be better hunters and better fishermen, and, above all, better equipped.

Falling in behind the boldly emblazoned "How To Do It" banners leading this endless and fascinating parade, we may stumble a bit, but we are being led to dizzying heights of all-around outdoor knowledge. For example, little did I know that some day I would be a well-read wilderness survival expert able to find my way unerringly through a howling Arctic blizzard finally to sit out the storm in a cozy snow cave, boiling up choice bits of my sealskin boots to chew on. For someone who gets confused taking out the garbage in a snowstorm, this is no little accomplishment.

Survival in the wilderness seems to be a hot subject these days, and it should be. Reminds me of the time I suddenly found myself a Naval Gunnery Officer teaching a World War II cram course called "Jungle Survival" to a bored class of aerial free-gunners soon to man their machine guns in flying Navy bombers over the South Pacific. My jungle experience at that point consisted entirely of tips I had picked up from "Tarzan of the Apes." Fortunately, as we began to method-ically tackle the "Jungle Survival Manual," my sleeping class suddenly came to attention when one of their shipmates graphically agreed with this "outdoor tip": "Don't forget to tie your shoelaces tightly around your ankles so your shoes won't snap off when your parachute opens."

Come to find out this young, top turret-gunner had lost a shoe when he bailed out of his disabled USN TBM bomber high over the jungle-covered mountains of New Guinea. He had then managed to make his way—traveling at night and hiding up by day—through the jungle and the Japanese lines with one bare foot wrapped in pieces of his parachute. He eventually reached the island coast and safety, the sole survivor of his crew. Needless to say, he became the instructor, and there were no more yawns from anyone in that class.

To return to the subject of more recent and relevant outdoor tips, I feel an obligation to pass along a few obscure but hard-won pieces of advice to my fellow outdoorsmen. Nowhere in today's vast library of sportsman's notebooks and hunter's almanacs do I find any warning whatsoever about how to sew suspender buttons on your hunting pants.

In my case, this potentially dangerous situation occurred when my wife, Ruby, had just patched my favorite, still-good-as-new hunting coat for about the fifteenth time. I then asked her, somewhat tentatively, to sew a few suspender buttons on a pair of hunting pants I had just relocated in the attic. "No thanks," she said. "Do it yourself. Use some strong thread and sew 'em on tight. You know how to do it."

So, how do you find some strong thread? In the medicine cabinet, of course. Dental floss! Then to my room, where I carefully sewed and knotted the six buttons on tight, two on each side and two in the back. Good, strong, prominent knots. Put on my new suspenders and I was ready.

Next scene: Opening day of the quail season. Your partner's new pointer decides to explore the entire southeastern section of the county, and you walk much farther than you had planned on a nice, hot day. At the lunch break, you begin to wonder what in the world is happening to the skin around your waistline. Chiggers? Briars? Something is boring six holes right through your shirttails and underwear, straight into your hide. Then you realize that those six suspender buttons, each armed with a hard, sharp knot of unforgiving, unrelenting dental floss, are out to get you. Taking off your suspenders won't help. And you can't cut off the buttons without making a big fuss of undressing since your partner might just—in fact, you know darn well he will—think it's about the funniest thing he ever saw. So you silently endure your "belt of thorns," walking a little sideways at times to change the cycle of abrasion for the rest of the torturous day. 31

Not much sympathy from your wife, either, when you finally get home. "Dental floss?" she laughs. "You'll probably get a good checkup."

The outdoor lore and woodcraft manuals usually have this to say about snowshoes: "Whose purpose is to distribute the weight of the body over a greater surface of snow than the sole of your shoe alone, thereby increasing support." Sounds logical, and it usually works that way, especially when you are flat on your back "distributing" your weight over a greater surface of snow with your snowshoes hung up in a tangle of willow brush. So watch out when experts say, "In areas of heavy brush, use the Michigan snowshoe."

Unless you are a double-jointed, Olympic-class, tumbling champion, heavy brush and snowshoes do *not* go together. I learned this hard lesson early in my career of "living off the land," a romantic definition of being cold, hungry, and miserable a good deal of the time.

And that's how I ended up on my back carrying a pack full of big No. 3 double, long-spring beaver traps, which were beginning to weigh about 75 pounds apiece as I continued to flounder around in the willows, "snowshoeing" my way out from Pine Creek to Wisconsin's Highway 55—a mere four miles away—where my cousin and trapping partner, "Red" Gordon Cummings, was waiting at the truck with the big 62-pound beaver he had taken out earlier on skis. (My cousin, that is, was on skis, *not* the beaver.) Skis were easier, even in the brush. And I'm afraid I finally got so frustrated with my brush-entangled snowshoes that I took them off completely and decided to wade out through the snow, whereupon I sank up to my waist in that lovely, cold, wet snow. For a while, I seriously considered staying right there and waiting patiently for the spring thaw. But since I'm here to write about it, I obviously got back on my snowshoes and, weeks later it seemed, made it out onto that beautiful, snow-packed highway to the truck. That was many years ago, and today even the sight of a dusty pair of decorative snowshoes on a cabin wall gives me a backache.

The memory of all this has exhausted me so with my last few "panting" and parting outdoor tips that I want you to remember to tie your shoelaces tightly around your ankles when you bail out of an airplane, don't use dental floss on suspender buttons, stay away from snowshoes and heavy brush, and, above all, keep in touch.

32

10 LAY NOT UP TREASURES— AND OTHER STUFF

IT was near that inevitable tax day in April. My wife, Ruby, and I had finally given up trying to understand the "easy to follow" rules for filing our joint federal income tax return and had gone in desperation to our friendly neighborhood tax advisor. In sifting through the maze of forms, funds and refunds, statements, checks, receipts, and other computerized mysteries, he eventually questioned Ruby on the forms she had filed, failed to file, or filed in duplicate until she said, "I distinctly remember filing the WD-40 Form."

The tax man said, with some surprise, "What was that you said?"

"The WD-40 Forms," Ruby said firmly.

The tax man, trying to suppress a grin said, "Oh, you mean the 1040 Form D. WD-40 is a rust preventative."

"And a very good one, too," Ruby said primly, which brought that discussion to a close.

When a can of rust and corrosion preventative used almost daily on all my hunting and fishing stuff gets mixed up with an official form from the Internal Revenue Service of the United States Department of the Treasury, you begin to realize how important and dominating the demands of maintenance have become in our daily lives. And what do we maintain? Ourselves, for one, from a root canal to athlete's foot. But the biggest cry is from the stuff we have somehow collected. It must be maintained; it demands attention. Just for the fun of it, I have been keeping track of the things that concern and receive my attention on a daily basis. Don't do it—unless you're ready for a surprise.

Not that I think breakfast conversation with your family

33

should revolve around the Monroe Doctrine or Aristotelian logic, but does it always have to center on the need to do something about crabgrass in the lawn, or the mower that won't start, or the left front tire on the car, or when the oil was last changed? Susan's sewing machine doesn't pick up the thread. Maggie has a dental appointment. Isn't it time for Bones to see the vet for shots? When you have a lot of stuff, you need to take care of it.

What's more, in spite of the Bible's warning to "not store up for ourselves treasures on earth, where moth and rust destroy, and where thieves break in and steal," we continue to store it up. Coming into this world as bare babes with nothing but the loving arms that held us, we certainly manage to collect a lot of stuff in this society of ours. Any of you who have faced the agonizing problems of moving from one house to another know what I mean.

How in the world did we amass all this stuff? Where did it come from? Some of us are collectors and others are advocates of "if you can't use it, sell it, give it away, or if that doesn't work, throw it away." Certainly a practical and sensible, down-to-earth attitude, but I think these people miss out on a lot of fun.

Take the case of my old friend and hunting partner, Carl Reinecke. Carl is a collector and his backyard and barn are wonders to behold. Not that they are full of junk. Carl has lots of good stuff. It's just that the opportunities to use a lot of his stuff have not yet occurred. For example, one day I found an ox yoke and a broken sundial in Carl's barn. "You never know when I'll need 'em," he said.

"Like when a pair of oxen might wander off the highway and into your yard, and you might want to yoke them up as a team and plow your garden?" I asked.

"That's right," Carl said seriously.

"Or the sundial," I continued. "The power goes off in your house and stops the electric clocks. Your wristwatch is busted so you come out here in the barn and prop up the sundial in the backyard to tell the time—if the sun is out?"

"You guessed it," he said and went on untangling the biggest bunch of tangled-up decoys I've ever seen.

"What happened here?" I asked.

"Last day. Freeze up. Sheet of ice moved 'em all down the bay. Sort of snarled up," he said and smiled. Carl likes maintenance. Gives him something to do.

What led me to all this philosophizing and muttering about "stuff"—an unelegant term for our material possessions, which too often own us—is a long series of maintenance disasters that have beset me lately. First, my almost-new outboard motor, carefully painted and camouflaged for use on my duck boat, suddenly gave up.

"Cracked ring scoured the lower cylinder," was the mechanic's grim diagnosis. And what they want for a new motor is the equivalent of what I could have once paid for a small ranch in Montana with a flock of Plymouth Rock chickens and a Fordson tractor thrown in.

I said to the mechanic, "I don't want to buy another boat, just the motor."

"That's right," he said. "Just the motor."

Times have evidently changed. But I remember what an uncle of mine used to say, "Sure, I can remember when beer was only a nickel. But I can also remember when nobody had a nickel." So, I've got to get a new motor—to add to my stuff.

And if that wasn't enough, my fairly new electronic wonder—the depth finder on my boat—consistently registers six feet. That's very reassuring when I'm skimming along over the shallow reefs here in Pamlico Sound—but I've got to get it fixed. Seems to me those hard-shelled reefs float around a lot out there. So, when I send in my depth finder for repair, I'm also sending in my (reading from the label) "Compact, programmable, 30-channel, three band FM monitor receiver," on which I can get only one station—the local NOAA weather channel. Loud and clear, which is very important down here when my forecasting friends, Frank Terrizzi or Charlie Compher, say, "Hurricane." We're gone. Off the Island with fervent hopes that our lifetime accumulation of stuff won't all blow away.

Remember what they said when old man Gotrocks finally died? "How much did he leave?" they said. "All of it!" was the reply.

11 IF AN ANGEL FLEW BY

IF you were lucky enough, a lot of you hunters are now trying out some of the newly developed outdoor clothing you received for Christmas instead of a hand-painted necktie, some nice handkerchiefs, or a ceramic key ring made especially for you by your "arts-and-crafts" daughter-in-law.

In an often lamentable world of plastic substitutes and man-made almost everything, some of you older birds will just have to admit that when it comes to the new hunting clothes and insulated boots, we never had it so good. It's much easier now to keep our old hides warm, dry, and comfortable; our feet warm enough to feel our toes occasionally; and a smile on our weather-wrinkled faces in spite of bone-chilling winds and rains.

No more bulky pads of wadded-up layers of clothes that once led my old hunting partner, Tom Marshall, when he saw me waddling out to join him and his decoys set out on an icy breakwater on Long Island Sound, to say, "A giant penguin if I ever saw one. Are those things your wings or your arms?" And, incidentally, you have never been cold until you've hunted in a wintry gale over salt water. Never.

But now with the truly miracle hunting clothes, like a breathable Gore-Tex parka lined with non-bulky Thinsulate, you have only to listen to my friend, Jim Lyons, who hunts ducks with a vengeance out on Hatteras Island, North Carolina, and wears one of the new parkas. "When it rains from the northeast on the Outer Banks, it rains *flat* . . . and in spite of the soaking-wet look of my parka, it doesn't stiffen up in cold weather. I stay dry, warm, and comfortable, and I don't get overheated whether I'm pushing a boat or just sitting still."

37

And it was Jim Lyons, who after endless hours of "just sitting still" under duckless and empty skies out on Pamlico Sound with his partner, Mike Cowal, finally stood up in the blind, stretched his six-foot, six-inch frame, and muttered to no one in particular, "If an angel flew by, I think I'd take a shot at it." That's what Mike reports, but Jim laughingly swears it was the other way around.

I've never worn one of the modern duck hunting parkas, but I once had an ancient Hodgman parka that time and hard use coated with a "natural camouflage" and a quality of its own. Over the years, the sun, wind, and rain plus splashes of outboard motor fuel and spilled coffee had produced a perfect copy of a muskrat house. All I had to do was put it on, walk out in the duck marsh with gun and shells, sit down on my wooden shell case, put up my parka hood, and wait. I was ready—a portable and wearable blind.

And then one tragic day, along came spring cleaning and, you guessed it, out it went. Stunned at my loss, I could only stare at my wife as she explained that it was definitely attracting rats to our garage. A real strain on the family tie, especially when I reluctantly purchased a new, light-tan, shiny-clean replacement that flared ducks the moment I took it out of the trunk of the car.

Unlike my old, natural-colored parka, everything seems to come completely camouflaged these days. Did you ever try to find a camouflaged thermos bottle in a fully grassed-in duck blind? And what about an old friend of mine who years ago bought what was then a "new-fangled" camouflaged hunting cap.

Long before blaze orange, he wore it for the first time on a woodcock hunt. "Without a dog," he said, "I always marked a hard-to-find dead bird by hanging my cap up in the alders and then working out and around from it until I found the bird. Well, I found the bird, all right. But to this day, I have *yet* to find that darned camouflaged cap!"

As I recall, the ever-widening use of camouflaged hunting clothes came out of World War II. "What war was that, Daddy?" my kids used to ask.

"World War II," I'd answer. "You must have heard about it. It was in all the papers."

Modern bowhunters use lots of camouflage, and it can be amazingly effective. Take it from me, they can really blend— or even melt—into their background on a deer hunt.

I'll never forget following Bones, my old Brittany spaniel, down a quiet and lonely logging road in the backcountry of northern Wisconsin. Not a soul around for miles, and I was just going along nice and easy, enjoying the solitude, when suddenly a voice right at the back of my neck said, "How you doing?"

For a startled second, I thought the devil had come to get me. I whirled around, wide-eyed and ready to fight—or better still, to run. And there stood what I *finally* made out to be a fully camouflaged bowhunter in the edge of the brush. He gave me a big grin from somewhere in that mass of brown lights and shadows, and I swear even his teeth looked camouflaged.

"Sorry to scare you," he said with a chuckle.

"Who *me?*" I said, still slightly shaken. "Not a bit. I always act this way when someone says 'hello' out of nowhere."

How my dog went right by him, I'll never know. He seemed—what I could see of him—like a pretty nice guy. Then, after a few more words, he stepped back into the brush and disappeared—literally. Never did get his name!

But with all the miracles of waterproof, breathable, non-rippable, briar-proof, and sometimes almost invisible cloth, there's nothing that matches my first canvas hunting coat. Presented to me on my 16th birthday, I think. I can still see the smiles of Mother and Dad at my surprise and delight when I unwrapped it to find it wasn't what I had been expecting—a sensible school jacket—but a genuine, new hunting coat. Not a hand-me-down, but my *own* hunting coat. I still have it in my closet. And although it's shrunk a lot around the middle, the sleeves are still all right. Every now and then, I pull it from its hanger and feel its friendly, soft, corduroy collar and stuff my hands in its big, roomy pockets. Well, I'm afraid words fail me on this one. They just don't make hunting coats like that anymore.

TWO HUNDRED BILLION BUCKETS 12

LIKE their stargazing, Stone Age hunting ancestors lying on a pile of skins at the mouth of a cave, the two grouse hunters are studying the brilliant star-filled sky above them. Flat on their backs in sleeping bags with Bones, their Brittany spaniel, curled up and softly snoring at their feet, we hear one hunter say, "Bill, how many stars are up there?"

"Go ahead and count 'em, George."

"Come on now, Bill. You used to teach this stuff. How many?"

"Well," Bill sighs. "Let's see now. Opinions vary, but the average estimate is 200 billion stars in our Milky Way galaxy."

"That brother-in-law of mine had a Ford 'Galaxy.' Used to ride the clutch all the time," George says.

Ignoring this, Bill continues. "A galaxy is a system or collection of stars. Our galaxy has a diameter of about 125,000 light-years, and since a light-year is the distance light travels in one year—or about 6 trillion miles—you just multiply 125,000 times 6 trillion and that makes our galaxy 750 trillion miles wide, and we're only one of 200 billion galaxies in the universe."

Suddenly a blazing, bright star streaks across the sky and then blinks out as George cries, "Hey! A falling star, I'll make a wish." He pauses, then adds, "Okay, I just wished it doesn't fall on me. Did anybody ever get hit by one of those things?"

"Meteorites? Only once that we know of. In about 1908, a nine-pound meteorite crashed through the roof of a house in Sylacauga, Alabama, and hit the housewife on her hip as she was taking a nap on the sofa. Fortunately, she was only slightly injured."

"Napping on the sofa? Would have missed her completely if she'd been working in the kitchen." George laughs.

"George, if your wife is still on that equal rights for women committee, I don't think I'd repeat that remark."

"Good point, Bill. Mum's the word," George laughs again. "Nine-pound meteorite, you say. About how big was the one we just saw?"

"Probably much smaller. The average meteorite is about the size of a 00 buckshot. Coming out of airless space, they approach the earth at about 137,000 feet per second, and the air friction in our atmosphere usually burns them up completely 30 to 50 miles above the earth."

"Double 0 buckshot at 137,000 feet per second. Wow! That would make even a wildcat reloader happy. Blazing bullets!"

"Good night, George."

"Just one more. I've heard that the earth is pretty small compared to all those stars and planets out there."

"It is. Comparing our earth to the sun is like comparing a BB to a basketball."

"BB, eh. I used to shoot 1¼ ounces of BBs on geese until I patterned them. Switched to number twos."

"That's nice. Now good *night*, George. It's been a hard day."

Ignoring this, George continues. "A basketball? How far away is the sun, and could we ever travel there?"

"It's about 93 million miles, and 'no' you couldn't travel there. You'd burn up . . . now wait a minute. If you're leading me into that old joke where you say, 'We'd go at night," I'm going to bat you over the head with this boot here."

"Okay, okay, I won't say it," George laughs. "But will we ever travel to another planet like Mars?"

"Who knows? One of the problems is provisioning the spacecraft. Going to Mars, landing and exploring, then returning to earth would take about 2½ years. And you would need to carry about nine tons of food, water, and oxygen per passenger."

"You mean tons of freeze-dried food? Stuff like that?"

"Probably. Why?"

"Don't you remember the time Sam fouled up our grub list on the elk hunting trip and we ate nothing but freeze-dried macaroni and Raisin Bran the last two days? I'm not going to Mars."

"Okay, I'll tell 'em. Good night, George."

"Just one more, Bill. Will the sun ever die out?"

"All kinds of theories. Some scientists believe that in about 50 billion years, the sun will eventually get so hot that all the planets, including ours, will melt."

"In *how* many years?" George cries out, raising up on his elbow.

"Shh! Quiet! You'll wake the dog and we've got Hawk Mountain to hunt tomorrow. I said in about 50 billion years."

"Billion! You really scared me. For a moment there, I thought you said 50 *million* years," and George falls back into his bag with a sigh of relief.

"For the last time, George, good *night*."

"Speaking of numbers, Bill," George persists. "Please tell me again how many stars are in the universe."

"George, promise me this is the last one."

"I promise."

"Okay now, listen to me. If you took a regular tablespoon and filled it with sand, it would contain about 1 million grains. And a bucket will hold about 1,000 spoonfuls, or a billion grains per bucket. Now fill up 200 buckets with sand, stand them up in your backyard, and each grain of sand represents one of the 200 billion stars in our galazy—just one galaxy. Now, do you want to know how many galaxies are believed to be in the universe?"

"I suppose I do."

"Okay, once and for all. It is estimated that there are 200 billion galaxies, so multiply the 200 buckets by 200 billion and you'll get 4 *trillion* buckets of sand with each grain representing a star in what we believe to be our universe."

After a long silence beneath the stars, George finally says, "What kind of buckets are we talking about?"

"Regular 12-quart buckets, I suppose. Why?"

"Oh, nothing. But I've just been thinking how hard it is to get a good, solid, galvanized, tin bucket these days. Plastic buckets just don't last. They tip over and . . ."

"Good *night*, George."

"Good night, Bill."

And finally all we hear is the soft snores of the three tired hunters and the gentle wind in the pines beneath the bright infinite sky.

13 HOW TO SIT UP IN A TREE

SILENCE. Absolute silence. A complete lack of sound. How seldom do we experience real silence in a noisy world? Silence that presses in on you from head to toe. Silence so thick that you could take out your hunting knife and cut out a small chunk up near your left ear just to let a little noise in—enough to let you know that you have not suddenly been left entirely alone, sitting up in a beech tree, in a dark and silent world.

Then in the faint predawn light a single yellow leaf spins and floats down past my tree stand where I sit like a big, dumb, camouflaged owl 10 feet above the floor of Whipping Creek Swamp in North Carolina. The leaf comes silently to rest below me, and I remember the question: If a tree falls in the forest and there is no one there to hear it—does it make any noise?

No woods noises. No bird song and no working wood-peckers to greet the dawn. I put my ear to the cool, smooth trunk of the big beech tree I'm sitting in and imagine I can hear the life-giving sap moving beneath the bark, flowing up from the deep roots to the topmost leaves of the tree . . . pulled up through the xylem cells by capillary attraction, I'll have you know, or is it the phloem cells? Or is it time to turn to the matter at hand—deer hunting?

It was an early start that put me up this tree to greet the new day. *Very* early, in fact. Maybe that's why golf is so popular. "Let's get a good, early start," they say. "Tee off at 8:30." No such civilized hours for deer hunters. Especially when Vernon Barrington and Joel Arrington (Barrington and Arrington? Sounds like a firm of London lawyers—or barristers, as they call them) are there to get you up and going. Vernon Barrington is the famous guide from Manteo, North Carolina, whose exploits as a hardworking fishing and hunting expert on the far reaches of Pamlico Sound, the tide rips and shoals of Oregon Inlet, the goose fields of Mattamuskeet, and the swamps of Eastern North Carolina, are legend. And then there's Joel Arrington whose card says "Outdoor Editor of North Carolina" and whose intimate knowledge of this great outdoor state is phenomenal. Years of Tarheel hunting and fishing have made his outdoor articles and brilliant photography completely authentic. A real pro and yet modest about it all.

But I hardly had any of these kind words in mind about Barrington and Arrington when they rolled me out of my cozy motel bed at 4:30 a.m., waited impatiently while I looked under the bed for my left boot, stuffed me, my rifle, and all my gear into Vernon's truck, and away the two of us went, while Joel took off with his camera. Forty-five miles—without coffee—and not much conversation to a lonely, logging road in the middle of a swamp under a moonless, starless sky right near Nowhere, North Carolina. When Vernon Barrington goes deer hunting, he doesn't fool around.

A silent departure from the truck, flashlight in hand, with a whispered warning to keep still, "Deer can hear you talk a long way off." No need. For once, I had nothing to say as I followed Vernon down the bank and in and out of a wobbly, cartop boat as we crossed the deep waters of the roadside canal. Then into the black swamp and along under the big hardwoods with a minimum of stumbling. Vernon claimed later that when I bumped into the unyielding trunk of a big swamp oak in the dark, I said, "Excuse me." Obviously an exaggeration. I might have said "sorry," but certainly not "excuse me." Although I *was* still pretty sleepy.

Then we suddenly stopped at the foot of a big beech tree. I looked up at what I thought was a lofty crow's nest hanging high up in the tree, but Vernon quietly assured me that it was *not* a crow's nest but my tree stand firmly attached to the tree trunk and only 10 feet off the ground. How Vernon located this particular tree in the midst of 7,862 trees that looked exactly alike I never asked. Guides have certain secrets.

So now to climb the tree. "Okay," Vernon whispers, "put your foot on this climbing iron. Now reach up for the next one. Watch it, watch it! Now feel up there for the next one.

Right above your hand. No—it hasn't fallen out. It's right there. Got it? Now only one more and you're right under the seat. Watch your head! Never mind. I'll get your cap later. Now grab the support and ease up onto the seat. Oop! Don't fall out now when we got you up this far." Vernon laughed. "Okay, let that line down and I'll send up your rifle and pack—and cap. You're on a good stand. Lots of fresh scrapes. Plenty of sign. Keep awake! See you at 10:30. Good luck!"

Ten thirty, he said. "That's four hours from now," I said to myself. If I sit in this position for four whole hours without moving, he'll have to get me out of tree and carry me back to the truck sitting on a folding camp chair—with my rifle still in hand.

As I watched Vernon's flashlight bob up and down through the swamp, I heard the sound of a paddle in the boat, the truck starting up and driving off, and then there was nothing. Silence had set in. The hounds of sound had yet to run me down. Gradually I relaxed. But eventually a high-flying mosquito found me and penetrated the palpable silence with a tiny, high-pitched whine at my right ear. Evidently a scout on a "search and drill mission," for it was soon joined by a full squadron of bloodthirsty attackers. It was then that I made the fatal error of reaching for my friendly can of Cutters and laid down a heavy screen of mosquito repellent mist in all directions.

Yes, deer hunters, you guessed it. No sooner had I put the Cutters back in my pack than I heard a deer crackling brush and faintly splashing in the shallow water directly behind me. As I slipped off the safety button on my rifle, a small, treacherous breeze came out of nowhere right smack in my face—and the sound of walking suddenly stopped. A long wait in the silence. All I could hear was my heart, and when I finally turned around, all I saw was the far-off white flag of a big swamp buck that didn't like the smell of Cutters.

Vernon nailed a nice five-pointer that morning, and I'm now working in the lab on a combination buck scent and mosquito repellent because I plan to go back and enjoy again the treetop silence of Whippin' Creek.

Garry Lloyd Goodson

14 LIFE ON THE OUTER BANKS

"**Y**OU say you're going to Outer Mongolia?" my old friend said with a smile.

"No! Not Outer *Mongolia*. The Outer *Banks* of North Carolina," I answered.

"Whatever for?" he asked in quiet wonderment. "At your age, too," he added, shaking his head. "And what about those storms?"

And now that we have left our old house in Connecticut with 30 years of good living to move down to Cape Hatteras, one of the barrier islands 40 miles off the coast of North Carolina, and have built a house on Pamlico Sound, I am making a list to answer my good friend's question about living on the Outer Banks—stormy as it often is.

The answers are many, but right now one of them stems from sitting here at my desk and looking out across the broad reach of a whitecapped Pamlico Sound. On this bright, sparkling, windy November day, I can see what seems to be an endless flight of cormorants moving in straggling flocks over the stakes of the fish traps at the mouth of Brigands Bay. I'm looking forward to the opening day of the waterfowl season because I remember what my new friend, Connie Reid Farrow, said. "When the cormorants begin to move in, you'd better start getting ready. It won't be long before the snows, Canadas, brant, and ducks show up."

Con Farrow, a spry and wiry 78-year-old, is famous for his intimate knowledge of the networks of freshwater ponds, sedges, and deep, treacherous bogs here on the island. An expert duck hunter, he told me that in all his years of carrying a shotgun in those trackless woods of loblolly pine, hornbeam,

47

live oaks, and dense bayberry bush interlaced with needle-sharp greenbriars that "sometimes got so thick you gotta go on your hands and knees," he never met a game warden. Not a single one. "Course, it might have been that I never came out of the woods the same way I went in," he said.

That could have been a pretty good reason because in those days, Con's idea of good duck hunting weather was a bright, moonlit night when the ducks came off the big sound back into the potholes. "Dusking," they called it.

Con's cousin, Buster Farrow, says, "Not only could Con find his way to the ponds in the pitch dark, but he was also quick and light enough to skip right over those bogs. Nobody could follow him."

"The secret of bog-trotting," Con says, "is to keep moving. When the bog begins to tremble and shake, don't stop. You've got to keep moving or you'll go in up to your neck." And I'd like to add another point. You must never weigh more than 138 pounds—like Con.

But times and the laws have changed, and as Con, now a widower, says in his warm, snug house and neat-as-a-pin parlor, "It was pretty hard for a lot of us to understand the game laws when they came in. But I see it different today. It's just plain necessary if we're going to keep on hunting. Now how'd you like a piece of fresh-baked apple pie?"

Twenty years in the Coast Guard on patrol boats and retiring as Ship's Cook—First Class, he certainly confirmed his rating with that piece of pie. Delicious! And when we got around to cooking and eating (one of my favorite subjects), Con told me how to cook a duck "Hatteras style."

"Two nice, fat birds will do. Stew 'em down good and thicken the gravy with a little cornmeal, salt, and pepper, of course. For the dumplings, you can use pie bread—pie-crust dough to you Yankees—or those new canned biscuits—if you have to. My wife used to add a rutabaga and an onion or two. Stew it all nice and low. We find it right good to eat. Now if you are going to make this a drum (channel bass) stew, you won't need the pie bread." But what you will need is plenty of room—it's wonderful but substantial.

Outer Banks names like Currituck, Hatteras, Pamlico, and Ocracoke are legend in the history of American waterfowl hunting. I first read about these places in my autographed copy of Van Campen Heilner's classic *A Book on Duck Shooting*. Written back in 1939, it has long been a well-worn, well-read favorite of mine. Illustrated with duck and goose hunting scenes painted by the old master, Lynn Bogue Hunt, and black-and-white photos by Heilner, it takes the reader from the lonely goose plains of Hungary in the delta of the Danube to fat mallards on the golden wheat fields of Alberta and then to the solid square miles of rafted waterfowl right here on Pamlico Sound.

In those days, the "off-island" northern gunners had to come by the Cape Charles boat to Norfolk, Virginia, and drive on a low-tide beach almost 100 miles south to Oregon Inlet to catch a small, rickety, three-car, flat-boat ferry. And then on down here to Hatteras . . . on the beach.

As Heilner says, "Eighty-five miles from a railroad, over a hundred by car, over no roads at all, the little settlement of Hatteras was almost as far away as one could go from anyplace without getting nearer to someplace else." I wonder what he'd think of today's Hatteras—paved roads, motels, and cable TV.

With this old book in mind, you can imagine how impressed I was to find out from my friend Luther Austin that he was once the manager of the famous and exclusive Gooseville Gun Club (with 3,200 acres right here in Hatteras) and that Van Campen Heilner himself was one of the four members. What's more, Lynn Bogue Hunt often showed up as Mr. Heilner's guest—sketch pad in one hand and shotgun in the other. Great shooting on the reef. "Fifty brant today," reads an entry in the old club log.

Luther Austin, now a mere 80 years old, who still keeps busy carving birds and building martin houses, remembers them all—the rich and often famous hunters like Rex Beach, writer and sportsman, who came down on a yacht with Luther's boss, G. Albert Lyon. Lots of memories and lots of stories.

But now the weather looks a little ominous, "making up" as they say. And the unknown poet who said, "Hatteras has a blow in store for all who pass her howling door" had evidently been here. But who cares? Just pass me a steaming bowl of that Hatteras-style stew and *let 'er blow.*

THE MAN WHO KNOCKS HEADS WITH A BOBCAT 15

"**Y**EARS ago in Connecticut, with 10 of our noisy, barking bird dogs penned up alongside the Congregational Church in New Canaan, Frank and I could have been called 'outside church members' because that's where we spent each service—'outside' with the dogs, trying to keep them quiet. Of course in warm weather with the windows open, we could hear the minister . . . and we even joined in on the singing of our favorite hymns." Ellen Weed laughed and then turned her full attention to feeding the two baby cougars in the family bathtub. Just weaned, the kittens tumbled over each other to reach the nipple of the baby feeding bottle full of a special formula.

There on the edge of Big Cypress Swamp, where the remnants of the Florida panther still roam together with plenty of wild pigs, turkeys, quail, and whitetail deer, live Frank and Ellen Weed together with Frank Jr. and Ellen's mother, Mrs. May Gale, an erect, smiling New England lady. A small ranch that raises cougars, bobcats, and wolves "so they will never become extinct" and with a pair of beautiful, light-green iguana lizards in a glass cage just above the kitchen sink, this is no ordinary Florida retirement ranch.

Both Frank and Ellen grew up in the quiet town of New Canaan, where young Frank soon found that pretty Ellen Gale, the girl across the street, had taught her cat to do tricks, raised pigeons and white mice, and shared his enthusiastic interest in animals and birds of all kinds. By then Frank, in spite of his tender years, was being recognized as a first-class handler and trainer of championship-class, field trial pointers and setters . . . and he spent more time than his family thought he should hunting grouse and woodcock in the wooded hills around town. The Weed family's coal-and-lumber business held little attraction for Frank although he did eventually receive a degree in business administration from the University of Miami.

Then Ellen added with a smile, "And for some reason or other, I have a degree in business, too. Imagine that. 'Business' for both of us. And the thing we *didn't* want to do was spend our lives in an office." A career they have both carefully avoided.

After their marriage in New Canaan in 1936, the Woods established one of the early and well-known shooting preserves in Connecticut, the Housatonic Game Farm in Brookfield Center. The brochure reads, "Pheasant, chukar partridge, and bobwhite quail hunting only two hours from New York City. Shoot over the most famous bird dogs in the world—the dogs whose pictures have appeared on 27 national magazine covers." But before you think of these dogs as strictly fancy models, many of them were field trial champions as well. "The dogs that have been admired on point at sportsmen's shows all over North America," according to the brochure.

But the act they'll never forget was Frank and Ellen's "invasion" of the most select and prestigious dog show in America held annually by the Westminster Kennel Club at Madison Square Garden in New York City. Invited to show "hunting dogs in action," the Weeds took not one, not two, but *ten* pointing dogs and their trained cock pheasant, Blackie, to the show.

With a flourish that probably upset generations of aristocratic Pekingese and Pomeranian dog fanciers, Frank and his pack of 10 pointers and setters swept the arena and performed beautifully—10 perfect, simultaneous points on Blackie hiding in a pile of cornstalks. Frank then flushed Blackie, who was trained to fly to another hiding place at the far end of the Garden. Whereupon with only a series of low whistles and clicks of his tongue, Frank put all 10 dogs at heel, and in perfect control, paraded the entire length of the area to where all 10 dogs found and perfectly pointed Blackie all over again. The applause was enthusiastic—"almost unrestrained," as one stern member later reported.

Having recently had some trouble parading *one* dog at heel, and never reluctant to ask for what some unthinking persons call "free advice," I did ask Frank if there was some secret or shortcut I was overlooking in my dog training program.

"No secrets. No cram course in dog training. Just time,   51 patience, and hard work," said Frank. "You and the dog have both got to like what you're doing. If it's no longer fun, go play golf."

Frank cannot only train bobcats (yes, bobcats—I saw him knock heads with a fierce-looking character that nuzzled him under the chin), whitetails, and rattlesnakes, he can train (will wonders never cease?) would-be shooters to hit what they shoot at. Just last week, I was talking to my fishing friend, Jim Askew, at Chokoloskee, and he well remembers Frank. "Back in 1961, he taught me and our Miami police class how to really hit with a handgun. And I saw his son, Frank Jr., hit an aspirin tablet in the air with a .22 rifle."

Like our friend, Lucky McDaniel, Frank is a proponent of the "instinct shooting" method, which boils down to, "Look hard at the target with both eyes. Point your foot where you want to shoot. And if your gun fits, you'll hit it. Try pointing your index finger fast at an object, and you're on it. The gun is merely an extension of your finger."

Trained by his dad as a kid in California on running jackrabbits, flying ravens, and crows, Frank Jr. is a spectacular aerial shot (hitting an aspirin tablet in the air with a .22 rifle is just one of his feats). He had his own shooting act at the sportmen's shows when he was only 15 years old. Today, he's an expert herpetologist, leatherworker, and accomplished gardener.

A session with the family photo album brought more of the Weed family into focus. With Frank out of the Marine Corps in 1946, we next see all five of the Weeds in full western garb as they appeared on their Miami TV show "Tumbleweed Ranch" with a full troop of Frank's trained animals. Fifty-six critters in all—bears, deer, alligators, raccoons, and monkeys.

The family group includes Frank, Ellen, Frank Jr., and Joyce. Joyce, as pretty as her mother and who is now Mrs. MacLaughlin of New Hampshire, still goes grouse hunting with her dad each fall around Utica, New York. (Frank is now a mere 68 years old, so the steep hills of the Mohawk Valley pose no problems.) Completing the group is a very young cowboy, Gary, who today is a professional engineer in Fort Lauderdale. His hobby, of course, is gun collecting.

All in all, a typically American family that knew what they wanted to do and then made it work. No wonder Ellen Weed says, "And I've enjoyed every moment of it."

16 HOW COME NO ONE HAS A CURE FOR BUCK FEVER

WITH all of today's forward strides in medical science, how come no one has come up with a cure for buck fever? As many of you hunters well know, a sudden onset of overall shakes and trembles, fixation of the eyeballs, and a gluing together of all your workable joints is only a partial definition of the dread malady. Buck fever, or buck ague as the old-timers called it, is not only brought on by what suddenly appears to your slack-jawed stare as the largest, fiery-eyed, steam-snorting buck in the western hemisphere, but it can happen to bird hunters as well.

It was long ago on a plantation near Waynesboro, Georgia, where the living was easy and the quail hunting was unbelievable. My host was Lon Davis, the traditional Georgia gentleman and sportsman. The birds were many, whirring up out of the broom straw over a pair of classic pointers. I thought I was finally getting used to that indescribable, nerve-shattering rise of a covey of quail until the day I walked confidently up to a pair of picture points and somehow right smack into the middle of the largest, noisiest covey of exploding bobwhites in the memory of modern man. They flew not only up, but sideways and crossways. They flew high, low, around me and all over me. Wings whizzed in my face and rattled against my gun, frozen in the ready position as I stood like a statue completely transfixed. Lon downed a pair, then turned to me and said, "Why didn't you shoot?"

"At what?" I asked, staring like I'd never seen him before.

"The quail," Lon replied.

"Oh, those," I said. "Too close. In fact, one of them flew out of my gun barrel."

"I think you had quail fever," Lon said, grinning.

"No sir, not me. Decided not to shoot. Too close," I said.

Lon Davis was a born storyteller, and I'm afraid that the big covey and the startled Yankee, namely me, became a part of his repertoire. But it could happen to anyone, I kept telling myself—and still do.

"Isn't he a dandy? Man, what a dandy!" Doc Cook whispered as he feverishly worked the lever of his Winchester Model 94 deer rifle, ejecting the cartridges out into the snow without firing a shot. Finally, the "dandy" big buck made one bounce and disappeared back into the brush. Then my Dad, who was acting as Doc's guide that day, pointed to the silent evidence of five unfired .30-30 cartridges sticking up out of the snow.

"How long do you think I've been doing that?" Doc asked in amazement.

"Buck fever, I guess. Could be one reason you haven't had much luck lately," Dad replied.

"For the love of Mike," Doc said, "I thought buck fever meant you couldn't pull the trigger—but I sure can *unload* in one hell of a hurry."

And then, as Dad told it, they both laughed, standing there years ago in the edge of big Cedar Swamp.

Buck fever has been known to follow many of us out of the woods and strike without warning in the more "civilized" phases of our everyday lives. One of its deadliest forms is the buck fever that attacks the would-be public speaker, who, gazing out at a sea of expectant, upturned faces, suddenly feels the speaker's platform shoot 300 feet above the crowd while he clings white-knuckled and speechless to the podium.

If by any long chance—and it would have to be a long one—you were a member of the Wilmington, Delaware, Volunteer Fire Department many years ago, you would have to remember the day your Department played host to the volunteers from the neighboring town of Dover. There were, I've been told, the usual games: firehose water fights, ladder climbing, and hand pumping competitions. And all this ended up in Wilmington's town square where hundreds had gathered to see the ceremonial presentation of the "Silver Fire Axe" by the Wilmington fire chief to the Dover fire chief as a gesture of goodwill to their neighboring fire fighters. After the usual flowery introduction made by the mayor of Wilmington, the two stalwart fire chiefs in full uniform strode out upon the stage. Then it happened to them both. Although they had bravely faced roaring flames, smoke, and danger, that awesome sea of upturned faces did them in. They stood and stared out at the crowd until the Wilmington chief, completely forgetting his carefully rehearsed presentation speech, finally blurted out, "Oh, hell, here's the axe!" and thrust it at the Dover chief, who grabbed it from the speaker's trembling hands, looked down at it in amazement and said, "Oh, is this the axe?"

And then there are the buck fever memories of attack on what was once my unassailable youthful confidence. Back in the '60s, I was the Remington Arms salesman in Chicago, calling on the big mail order catalog houses. Somehow I found myself scheduled as the Remington sporting ammunition demonstrator on a *live* WGN Chicago television show called "Test Lab," sponsored by Spiegel, our good customer. At the show's rehearsal, under regular studio lights, I shot a Remington "High Velocity" hollowpoint .22 cartridge into a bar of Fels Naptha soap set up in a bullet trap to demonstrate the "hard-hitting, mushrooming power of this remarkable little cartridge." All went well at rehearsal, and I hit the soap with a resounding *splat*. In fact I was so smiling, glib, and confident that the show's director asked me if I'd be interested in joining the staff.

Then came the *live* TV show. No retakes, no fixing the film. What you did was what you got. Suddenly, I was on the air, *live* in hundreds of thousands of living rooms, with the blinking red eye of the TV camera aimed directly at my Adam's apple, which began to rise and fall at the same speed as the blinking light. When my voice finally reappeared, it sounded to me like Mickey Mouse speaking from inside a steamer trunk. And when I turned to make the rifle shot, to my already growing sense of horror, the overwhelming glare of the TV lights completely obliterated my front sight. I could see the soap but not my sight. After what seemed like several hours, I finally aimed along the side of the barrel and fired. Then the twist of fate that had placed me in this predicament untwisted. I hit the soap square in the middle, and, glory be, my voice returned.

"Thought you had a misfire," said my dad, who was at home with all my family proudly watching the show.

Stangely enough, no more offers to join the staff were made to me. Makes me nervous just to think of it. Don't talk to me about buck fever, friends. I've been there. 55

17 QUAIL IN THE RAIN

So much has been written about the glories and infinite pleasures of bobwhite quail hunting that there is not much left to say—but I'm going to try to say it anyway. Unless you've been there, it's hard to picture the high style and sweep of a pair of finely trained pointers or setters working carefully, but swiftly, ahead of the gun through the sunshine and shade of a Georgia piney wood. You can almost hear their eager nostrils "pop" as they search the sweet, promising air for the elusive scent of a bobwhite quail, the splendid little game bird no bigger than your fist. Then suddenly that greatest of canine miracles—the point! And the heart-stopping *whir* of the covey rise. Unforgettable!

But isn't it remarkable how far we've come with that most faithful of friends, the hunting dog. It all started, they tell us, ages ago when we shared our cave in a savage partnership with a half-wild, wolf-like dog. Somehow our hairy, bettle-browed ancestors and their dogs shared the hunt and the kill, yet bonded that strange and amazing loyalty that has remained unchanged down through the years. How can you possibly compare that to the highly ritualized pursuit of the bobwhite, no more than a single gulp to a hungry dog but with a fascinating scent strong enough to turn a hard-running bird dog almost inside out when his remarkable nose says "whoa"? How can you compare that with raised hackles, a snarling growl and a piercing howl, and the bared, long, sharp fangs of the cave dog when he struck the scent of a giant cave bear or a saber-toothed tiger? And then, if the kill was made and they both were still alive, how did they share the raw meat?

57

I have a hunch that the division of the kill was a lot more equitable than that piece of biscuit with a dab of quail gravy you tossed your hunting dog when your wife wasn't looking. But come morning in the cave and another hunting day, I'll bet that the wolf dog pricked up his ears and rose with a yawn and a stretch from his bed by the fire when his man picked up his spear and went to the mouth of the cave to check the weather. Regardless of the weather, they left the cave together. Isn't that how your dog acts, too, when you show up with gun in hand in the worst of days? And, finally, when a cave dog's hunting days were over and man and dog went afield no more, I wonder if the caveman carried somewhere in his savage heart the same memories that we carry in ours?

Quail hunting was not especially designed for pouring rain, but that was what we encountered when my hunting partners, Mike and Nancy Cowal, and I set out before dawn on a dark and dismal January day to join our quail hunting friend, Maynard Harrell, over on the mainland in Plymouth, North Carolina. So hard did it rain that halfway through our 150 mile trip, we stopped to call ahead and see if Maynard was really going to hunt.

"Why not?" he said. "Come on ahead, it may clear up later this afternoon."

And it might not, too, I thought. Maynard, a prominent young attorney, is also well-known as a dedicated hunter. He has the only living room I've ever seen that is completely furnished with the heads of trophy-size whitetail bucks. Obviously an all-day downpour and flooded roads were mere details when a man planned to go bird hunting.

Maynard reminds me a lot of our friend, Jim Lyons, here in Buxton who has been known to stand up in his duck blind during a driving, drenching downpour with the rain dripping off the end of his nose and say, "Looks like it *might* clear up this afternoon," as he pours the water out of the end of his barrel. In fact, his remarkable wife, Marcia, is reported to have said that if Jim had been around during the Flood, he would have shot the ducks off Noah's Ark. And if there is any doubt about Jim's love of duck hunting, their cute, curly-headed, two year old son is named Patrick *Teal* Lyons.

And so with Maynard's hopeful weather report in mind, we continued on across empty miles of flat coastal marshland with the windshield wipers of Mike's truck going full tilt while Nancy took a nap. Our welcome was cordial at the Harrells', and after a quick cup of coffee from Debbie, Maynard's pretty wife, we took off. Following them both in their hunting truck, complete with gunracks and three bird dogs in the crate, we rode out onto the rutted, muddy roads, glistening in the rain, that lead across the thousands of acres of ditched and drained farmlands that surround Plymouth.

Our first stop was to pick up Maynard's hunting partner, Milton "Gator" Elliott, and his well-known chocolate Lab, Cocoa, who retrieves everything from Canada geese to doves to quail to bullfrogs. (Bullfrogs? That's right. To get a mess of delicious, fried frog legs all you do is drive along the ditched road on a summer night and "shine frogs." A pair of frog eyes shining in the light, and a .22 rifle does the rest and then Cocoa, all 90 pounds of him, goes into dynamic action. Down the bank, into the ditch with a mighty splash and soon he's back to the truck with a three-ounce frog— and all in great style.) Gator and Cocoa had been whiling away a few hours dove hunting in the rain, waiting for us, and the bulge in Gator's wet game coat showed they had actually bagged a few birds in spite of the weather. "Gator is the best wingshot I ever saw," says Maynard. "And I'm not exactly a beginner."

It was a pleasure to see the three perfectly trained, faultless, responsive bird dogs in action. There was Rebel, a dignified, middle-aged, Brittany; the promising young setter, Pete, in his first year with Maynard; and Gator's high-tailed, veteran setter, Buster. Trotting along in front of the truck, they slammed into skidding points on the muddy road, beautifully backed by the other dogs. And the quail were there. We all shot well, even Mike and Nancy who were new at the game. In fact, I always shoot very well when I'm shoulder to shoulder with shots like Maynard and Gator. For a while I thought the birds I claimed could possibly have been hit by the experts, but I soon put that thought aside.

And so we bring this quail-in-the-rain episode to a wet but happy close. It rained all the way home, too, 150 miles of it.

MY BROTHER BOB 18

Ⅰ T'S a long way from Hudson, Wisconsin, to Buxton, North Carolina, but my brother, Bob, and his wife, Jean, just came to visit us out here on the Outer Banks. We hadn't all been together since 1981, and there was a lot to catch up on. Talk of our children and grandchildren, thumbing through old photo albums just "remembering when," and friendly crossword puzzle competitions between my wife Ruby and Jean, who can do *The New York Times* crossword puzzle in an amazing one hour!

All this plus fishing, of course, kept us busy for one short week. A longer stay was difficult because Bob, a retired ad man, and Jean run Bob Mitchell's Fly Shop in Lake Elmo, Minnesota. They specialize in fly-tying, fly-casting lessons, and fly-fishing tackle, including flies, leaders, rods, reels, lines, waders, jackets, creels, thermometers, clippers and all the other marvelous gadgets the well-dressed fly-fisherman must hang on his or her person before setting out to stalk the wily trout or battle a big bass. Their daughter, Cathy Dicharry, eminent fly-casting instructor and professional flytier, took time off from her family and job as a medical specialist to tend the shop and give her folks a chance to get away for a short vacation.

And before you hunters begin to wonder what all this has to do with hunting, listen carefully. According to Bob, you can easily become a real hero and important guy to your fly-fishing friends, many of whom are flytiers, too. The answer is the fur and feathers we all—hopefully—collect each fall. Did you know that a wood duck skin, properly prepared, brings about $35 in the fly-tying market? And "proper preparation" is easy. Just borrow a little of your wife's borax laundry powder and sprinkle it on the flesh side of a bird or animal skin. It seems that just about every piece of fur or feather has some use for that fly-tying friend of yours. Body feathers, tails, and wings from pheasants, grouse, ducks, geese, and all the other feathered game you hunt can easily end up on a hook in the flytier's vise as the trout fly—a dry, wet, nymph or streamer that emerges from the nimble fingers of the artist. (A cruel critic of my fly-tying once referred to my trout flies as being "bunched" rather than tied.) And the hair from the cottontail rabbit or squirrel, or the hollow hair of the big deer, may float a stream or pond as a high-riding bug or a kicking hair frog to fool a big bass.

But before you decide to turn all that fur and feather into ready cash, Bob suggests you check your state game laws. It's okay to give them away, but an outright sale may be illegal. On the other hand, a free-handed gift of fur or feathers you were going to throw away may bring, in return, a welcome mess of fresh caught trout, bass, or bluegills next spring as well as the gratitude of that flytier.

And now, gentle reader, be prepared for a complete change of subject. (I can see my editor pushing back his green eyeshade and gripping my copy with both hands.) When my kids were little, but old enough to be smart alecks, they would say, "What war is that, Daddy, that you're talking about?"

"World War II," I'd say. "You must have heard about it. It was in all the papers."

Not long ago I was poking through a stack of really old *National Geographic* magazines and found a January 1947 article by J. Frank Dobie (now a famous writer) about post-war Germany entitled "What I Saw Across The Rhine." One of the things he saw was the city of Old Heidelberg with its world-famous museums, art galleries, and ancient university still intact. The caption beneath the photo reads, "Spared the devastation of war, Old Heidelberg remains a citadel of learning." And then, "Because of its cultural and historical importance and lack of major industry, the venerable university city was not bombed by the Allies."

And now for a statement never written before. Heidelberg was saved from destruction and not "bombed by the Allies" because of my brother Bob, and 15 seconds. He was First Lieutenant Robert C. Mitchell, one of the lead bombardiers of the 303rd Bomb Group, Hells Angels, 8th Air Force, flying B-17 bombers and based in Molesworth, England.

Here's how it happened. In the spring of 1945, about March 1 as Bob recalls, enemy targets for the day were listed as No. 1 Primary and No. 2 Secondary. At the preflight briefing early that morning, the German city of Heidelberg suddenly showed up as a secondary target. Up to then it was considered a nonmilitary target, but now it was listed as an enemy target to be bombed.

Obviously, no one openly questioned this change in Heidelberg's status. No one questioned the possible destruction of this "citadel of culture and learning." (There were no suggestion boxes in the United States Air Force at that time.) The target had to be seen through the Norden bombsight—Bob's bombsight to be specific because as a lead bombardier he took full command over the target and the other bombers released their loads when they saw him drop his bombs.

The secondary target, however, could be bombed through cloud cover using radar to locate it. So if the primary was hidden by clouds you went to the secondary target regardless of cloud cover.

As the formation of 36 B-17 bombers, each carrying 3,000 pounds of high explosives, approached the primary target—a railroad marshaling yard near Heidelberg—they found it socked in with a heavy overcast of clouds. Bob started down the bombing run and stared down through his Norden bombsight to the solid clouds below. He told me, with some urging because he's usually been reluctant to talk about his war experiences, "I took them as far as I could, right up to the last. I had already depressed my mike button to end the run and go to Heidelberg when suddenly the thick cover opened for about 15 seconds and we dropped our bombs."

The next day Heidelberg was scratched from the target list.

Now, if you want to stop in at Bob Mitchell's Fly Shop, Taylor Building, Lake Elmo, Minnesota, and purchase a few well-tied #22 Light Cahill trout flies, or maybe just to surprise him by mentioning Heidelberg and those important 15 seconds, help yourself. In either case, both he and Jean will be glad to see you. It's that kind of place. Bob's quite a guy, and what's more, I'm proud to say he's my kid brother.

19 HENRY BAUMGARTNER AND HIS DAY BEFORE CHRISTMAS HUNT

IT was the first Christmas since Ellie had gone that Henry felt like doing anything at all about the silent and still strangely empty house. He and Lucy, the old coon and part-time rabbit hound, had gone down to the south pasture, cut a nice, fat balsam, and brought it back on the truck. Now it sat there on the back porch, its green branches lightly decorated with snow, sparkling in the sunshine as though waiting to be invited into the parlor.

The mail had just arrived, and Henry sat there at the kitchen table opening a letter from his daughter, Mary, with hands that trembled a bit. Reading the letter, his spirits sank. Her husband, Joe, had drawn the Christmas shift at the power house in Pine City, and it was too far over those icy winter roads for Mary and the two kids to come down alone. And they really couldn't leave Joe on Christmas. But they would come down later, for sure, when the roads got better. Finally, they all wished Granddad a "Merry Christmas."

As Henry sat there in the quiet kitchen with only the ticking of Ellie's old clock to break the silence, he looked out through the window at the waiting tree on the porch and said with a deep sigh, "Merry Christmas." Lucy, as though sensing his feelings, got up slowly from her box by the stove (the box was a special dispensation from Ellie; Lucy had been her favorite), came over and put her gray muzzle on Henry's knee, rolled her age-dimmed eyes up at him, and whined.

"Want to go out, old girl?" Henry asked, rubbing his gnarled hand behind her briar-torn ears. Henry opened the door, and as Lucy went carefully down the steps with her stiff hips, she turned and barked. A single, demanding bark.

"You want to go hunting? Chase a rabbit? Is that it?" With that, Lucy put her nose to the snow-covered ground and, after a few sniffs, stopped as if to say, "Let's go."

"Okay, I'll get my gun. Better than sitting 'round here."

Soon the two old hunters were making their way across the field. Henry, his old pump gun cradled in his arm, picked his way carefully over the plowing, favoring his left knee that didn't seem to bend right, while Lucy worked out in short casts ahead of him, popping her nose along the frozen

ground. Henry noticed her hips seemed to be working better.

"Save your nose there, Lucy," Henry called. "We'll go try the edge of Cedar Swamp."

They had gone about halfway across the field when the silence was suddenly broken by the far off excited yips of beagle hounds hot on the track down in the swamp.

"Sounds like the Hoff boys and their beagles," Henry said, as he and Lucy stopped. "If it's a snowshoe, they're in for a real chase. No easy circles like a cottontail. Let's go see."

Shortly, they stopped again to watch a big, white snowshoe hare bolt out of the swamp. Up and over the plowing in great bounds, it disappeared into a brush-filled ditch.

"Now we'll see if those little hounds can figure that one out," Henry said to Lucy. The sound of the hounds and the sight of the hare had made Henry's knee loosen up a little.

"Hey, Mr. Baumgartner," came a call from the edge of the woods as Henry's two young neighbors, Finn and Erik Hoff, stepped out into the field. "Merry Christmas!"

Henry fully meant to return their cordial greeting, but the words stuck in his throat. He finally managed to say, "Hi, boys. How you doing?"

"Not so good," Finn replied. "We can start 'em all right, but with old Smokey gone, these three young ones make a lot of fuss . . . and then lose the track. Just pottering around."

"And there they are, doing it again," Erik said, pointing down the field where the three beagles were circling around out on the plowed ground with excited yelps and furiously wagging tails—each on its own mission.

"Hey, you cabbage heads," Finn yelled as he approached the dogs. "Stop using your tails and start using your noses. Come on, Lucy, see if you can help these *dumbhunders.*"

With that, Lucy joined the hunt, swung off to the left, and immediately struck the track with a deep, bellowing bawl that made your hair stand on end. And away they went. Lucy moving like a youngster, down into the ditch and back into the swamp . . . in full cry.

"See you at the truck! We're up on the County Road," Erik yelled, following Finn as they tried to get ahead of the chase.

For a moment, there was a sharp regret that he was no longer young and no longer running with the hounds. But then Henry thought of Lucy's sudden but probably temporary "rejuvenation" and laughed out loud. The first time in days.

Now, he might as well hunt alone. After a few careful

kicks of a brushpile with his good leg, out popped not one but two cottontails, and Henry rolled them both. At least I can still shoot, he thought. Later, back at the truck, tired but with four cottontails in his hunting coat, he heard a single shot.

Soon, "the hunt" appeared down the road, the little hounds tugging on a leash, followed by Finn and Erik, and Lucy a poor third. Finn held up the long-legged hare and called, "Thanks to Lucy!"

It took both the Hoff boys to lift a tired Lucy up into the truck bed. But her tail was still wagging, and she had enough steam left to snap at a too-friendly male beagle. On the way back to Henry's house, the Hoff boys invited him to come by on Christmas for a mug of *glogg*, the traditional Norwegian holiday drink. But the thought of the empty house awaiting Lucy and him was too much to come back to on Christmas.

"No thanks," he said. "I got the chores to do."

"The way Mama makes *glogg*, Mr. Baumgartner? You're missing something, you know. Two mugs and you want to go out and roll in the snow."

No more was said until they turned at the foot of the hill and spotted a car in the driveway. Henry's heart leaped up and his voice trembled as he said, "Is that Joe's car?"

And it was. As they drove up, young Joe and little Ellie exploded out the back door and down the porch steps crying, "It's Granddad and Lucy, too. Merry Christmas!"

As Henry remembers, it was all a warm and happy haze. The tree was off the porch and in the parlor; a hard hug from Mary and a slap on the back from Joe that almost knocked him down; the kids hanging onto his tired legs. All he could say was, "We didn't think you were coming."

"Joe traded shifts with your old friend, Larry Madison. Wasn't that nice of Larry," Mary said with a smile so much like her mother's that Henry could hardly stand it. But he recovered enough to lean into the window of the truck and say, "A Merry Christmas to you both. And, by golly, you save me some of that *glogg*, too, you hear."

And off went the smiling Hoff boys back down the rutted road.

THERE'S NOTHING WRONG WITH 20 DOING NOTHING

ON a sunny day in late summer, the young man stopped in front of the neat, white house set back from the tree-lined street. He looked carefully at the street number on the gate post of the picket fence, checked it against his clipboard, and opened the gate and went up the path. Before he reached the front porch, he was greeted by a wiggling, black Labrador pup that attacked his shoes and jumped at his clipboard. Behind the eager pup came an adult black Lab, obviously the pup's mother. She stopped, looked intently at the visitor, gave one welcoming but cautious bark, and sat down to wait as the young man stood stock still, holding his clipboard high.

The screen door on the porch opened, and a smiling, gray-haired lady came out. She wiped her hands on her apron and said, "Don't worry. The dogs are friendly. Oh me! That pup Amos is too friendly. Amos, stop it."

"They are very nice, but I'm somewhat allergic to pets," the caller said, nervously keeping his eye on the dogs. Then, regaining his composure, he asked, "Is your husband, Mr. Bartlett, in?"

"Yes, I think he is. Out in back probably," she said. "Look on the sunny side of the house. Or he could be in the barn fussing with his everlasting duck decoys."

"Oh, does he hunt?" the young man asked.

"Does a fish swim?" the lady said with a sigh as she went back into the house.

The caller, followed by the two dogs, walked along a path to the back of the house where he found Mr. Bartlett stretched out on one of two faded canvas lounge chairs, faintly snoring in the warm sun. As he approached, Mr. Bartlett slowly opened one eye and without moving said, "Hi there. What are you selling?"

"Mr. William Bartlett? Sorry to bother you. I'm not a salesman. I'm psychological interrogator Peter Hawkins, Ph.D. I'm doing field research in 'The Traumatic Effects of Retirement on the American Male.' "

"The heck you say," Mr. Bartlett said as he smiled and sat up slightly. "Sit down, Pete. Come on, Amos, leave Dr. Hawkins alone. Sue, take care of your pup. And, incidentally, how did you get my name? And you can call me Bill."

"From the computer," said Peter. "You fit all the requirements for Level I on age, education, former occupation, and income level before and after retirement."

"Well, isn't that nice," Bill said. "But sit down anyway. You don't want to waste this sun. Going to rain tomorrow—according to this knee of mine."

Peter sat down gingerly on the old lounge chair and almost disappeared in the canvas folds.

"Your knee," Peter asked, "as a weather indicator?"

"Infallible. Ever since I stepped in that muskrat hole." As Peter started to make a note on his clipboard, Bill added, "Muskrat is one word."

"I'm fully aware of that," Peter said primly. "Merely recording your obvious attachment to folklore and superstition. Part of your computer profile."

"Put down, too, that my knee often outperforms the weather satellite," Bill said with a grin. "Matter of record."

Ignoring Bill's suggestion, Peter continued, "I presume that you have taken the advice of retirement counselors and pursued a meaningful and purposeful hobby."

"Of course," said Bill. "I pursue ducks, deer, rabbits, ruffed grouse, brook trout, and an occasional walleyed pike."

"You mean to say that you hunt and fish every day? What do you do when it rains or the seasons are closed?"

"Nothing," Bill said.

"Now, look Mr. Bartlett. This is an official, fully accredited questionnaire, and it specifically asks, I quote, 'Other interests and activities.' I just can't put down 'Nothing.' "

"Why not?" asked Bill.

"Because it's not constructive. It's not consistent with the truly American work ethic. You just can't work every day for forty years and then suddenly stop."

"I did," Bill said. "There's nothing wrong with doing nothing."

"But didn't you feel any community responsibility? Volunteer work, for example?" asked Peter.

"I tried it. I'm a retired crane operator. Not much call for that at the senior center. Wasn't much at envelope stuffing, either. My thumbs are too big. So I just drop off a mess of fish or a hunk of venison now and then. It works better."

"Now, about doing nothing. At your age, the rigors of the chase no doubt are exhausting, and doing nothing allows you to recuperate when you're not hunting or fishing. Correct?"

"Not at all. I've learned to do nothing when I'm actually hunting or fishing," said Bill.

"Excuse me, but isn't that a puzzling juxtaposition? Doing nothing while you're busily doing something?"

"Okay, Dr. Hawkins. Sit back—all the way back—and relax while I tell you how I do it.

"Take the business of learning how to do nothing while you are sitting perfectly still in the woods. You've got to sit there until you can feel the woods sort of taking you in. So you can feel the earth itself coming up through the soles of your boots. That fellow, Thoreau, said something about 'Shall I not have intelligence with the earth? Am I not partly leaves and vegetable mould myself?' Next step is learning how to look around when you're doing nothing. I used to sit way out on the edge of that bench in my duck blind all day long, rotating my neck like an old horned owl, constantly on the lookout for a shot. Even on dull days when Sue had given up and gone to sleep. Wore me out. Then my daughter got one of those pocket guide bird books. She sneaked it into my hunting coat pocket. Said that if I couldn't shoot a bird and eat it, I didn't know what it was. So I tried it, and now I can tell a swamp sparrow from a song sparrow as easily as I can tell a canvasback from a Canada goose. Taught me to sit back and enjoy the entire marsh. Look around and just do nothing. Just relax and be there. Do you see what I mean, Pete? Pete. Hey, Pete!"

But Pete had gone to sleep in the sun. Bill chuckled to himself, leaned back farther in his canvas couch, and shortly joined him. Just doing nothing.

21 WHEN EVERYONE WORE HATS & CARRIED POCKET KNIVES

DO you remember when everybody wore hats? When probably the only bareheaded people you saw were fleeing from a burning building or walking across the front yard in the summertime to visit the mailbox? No one considered himself fully dressed for the outdoors unless he wore a hat. Women even wore hats indoors at bridge parties or when they went to church, and as for the outdoors, the only hatless lady I ever saw was a farmer's wife feeding the backdoor chickens. (Evidently the new puppy had made off with her sunbonnet). These days a lady's hat is a rare sight. Pretty Martha Chapman wore a new hat to church here in Buxton several Sundays ago, the only one in the congregation, and received so many compliments that she said to my wife, "I'll have to wear this again." But she hasn't.

When I try to picture men's faces from long ago, they all involve their hats . . . permanently placed. The kind of hat that when rarely removed revealed a broad band of untanned brow that completely changed a man's looks. "Sorry, Clayt. Didn't recognize you without your hat," was a quite common apology.

I'm glad to report that in these recklessly bareheaded days you rarely see a hunter without a hat, or the conventional hunting cap. Evidently, most of us have learned that if you keep your feet and your head warm, you're usually warm all over. And we haven't gone in for any fancy modern changes, either, when it comes to caps. Looking through some 40 year old hunting photos lately, I was glad to see the hunters, including my dad, wearing much the same caps that are worn today. Not camouflage or brilliant hunter's orange, but

71

the same old, visored khaki cap with a variety of earflaps. Flaps in front or tied on top with a bow or the turndown-all-around type of brim. That's the style I have preferred ever since the day I stood at the counter of Hansen's Dry Goods Store and heard Dad say, "You got a hunting cap here to fit the kid? It's about time he had his own."

And it was about time, too. I'd been wearing somebody's old hand-me-down hunting cap for years, it seemed, with a brown sock sewed around the inside band by my mother to keep the peak out of my eyes. So I stood there in silent, grinning anticipation as Mr. Hansen brought down a big box of caps from the shelf behind him and searched for a size to fit the kid. And when he found it, I was delighted to see that it was an exact copy of the cap my dad and Bill Wenzel, the only duck hunting guide in town, always wore. The kind where you could turn the canvas brim down all around to keep your ears warm and the icy sleet off the back of your neck, as you imagined yourself silent and watchful in a duck blind on the far-off side of the lake.

It was Saturday when I proudly wore my new hunting cap out of the store and down the street, and then took the long way home in order to meet and greet as many people as possible with a casual salute of my finger to the brim of the new cap. And although Mother absolutely refused to let me wear it to Sunday school the next day, I actually looked forward to school and wearing my new cap on Monday.

That night I put my cap on the bedpost. I can still see it hanging there in all its glory as I looked up from reading "Tom Swift and His Electric Rifle" for the third time. With that great passage about Tom and his elephant hunt in Africa when he turned his electric rifle up too high, and the shot completely dissolved the elephant leaving only the giant ivory tusks. I knew, of course, that it wasn't true, but I always dreamed of hunting in Africa even without an electric rifle. And now if I ever got the chance to go, I'd wear my new cap regardless of the merciless African sun and the advice of my British white hunter, "Better wear your sun helmet today, old chap. Nasty bit of glare, you know."

"No thanks," I would say. "I'll just wear this old cap from Hansen's Dry Goods Store."

When it comes to hunting clothes it's pretty hard to beat the memory of your first and very own hunting cap, but do any of you remember the unsung merchandising genius who put a neat, buttoned-up, little leather pocket to hold your jackknife on the side of kids' high-top leather boots? And do you remember your overwhelming desire to own such boots . . . especially when the two-bladed jackknife came with the boots absolutely *free*?

Again the scene is Saturday at Hansen's and you and your dad are sitting in the boot and shoe section waiting for Mr. Hansen while you wiggle your toes in the neatly darned woolen socks, carefully inspected by your mother that morning. "I'm not sending you out in public to expose your bare toes. What would people think!" she said. When Mr. Hansen came and measured your foot he said, "If he grows up to match his feet he'll be a big one."

Although you were somewhat excited by the idea of new boots, it was pretty much of a routine shopping mission until Mr. Hansen opened a big yellow box marked "Free Two-Blade Jackknife Enclosed" and took out a pair of brown, beautifully oiled, high-top boots with a buttoned-down knife pocket on the outside right boot. Never to be separated. You could die with your boots on and never lose your knife. You were stunned with desire. Completely hooked. And when your dad hesitated after looking at the price tag, you desperately promised to mow the lawn, weed the garden, and do your homework every night for the next 40 years. After a few sighs from dad, the boots—and the knife—were yours.

The boots were in the big, yellow box under the bed with the knife newly oiled, snug in its pocket, and then you dreamed that you were "North of 59°," in the dead of winter when you and your partner were driving a dogsled on a long and desperate trek to reach your old friend, Trapper Joe, and his beautiful half-Cree daughter, Moon Beam, who had sent a wireless message that her father had pneumonia. They had run out of grub, were completely snowed in, and doomed to starvation. Then somehow you lost both your knife and your axe down a crevasse in "Froze to Death" glacier and faced a cruel and fireless overnight camp in the willows. No knife to build a fire! Then you looked down at your boot. (You guessed it, your knife was still there.) And then with a life-saving, tin cup of hot tea at your chapped and bearded lips, you cried out in the arctic stillness, "Here's to Mr. Hansen's—the best dry goods store in town."

22 HANG UP YOUR LONG UNDERWEAR IN THE LOBBY

A flight of mallards working hard into a northwest wind crossed the full moon that shone down on the small house trailer. This hunter's hideaway was set back off a single-lane dirt road that wound down to the flooded timber along the banks of the mighty Mississippi between Illinois and Missouri.

Gently rocking in the wind and with streamers of wood smoke trailing from the tall, stovepipe chimney, the old trailer was evidently well occupied. Even above the whistle of the wind, you occasionally could hear a chorus of duck calls that suddenly changed into howls of laughter when the door swung open and one Paul Stroud threw what appeared to be a small canvas cot out into the yard. He shook his fist at it and went back in.

All this at least 35 years ago, but I still laugh out loud when I remember Paul and his new compact, lightweight, collapsible, "folds down to the size of a camp stove" canvas cot. It was one of the newest items from the prestigious dealer Von Lengerke and Antoine of Chicago. Paul, senior buyer and department manager, was also a champion duck caller, expert flytier, professional dog handler, and veteran camper, so he often field-tested the company's new products.

With eight perspiring (the stove worked *very* well), practicing duck callers and two damp Labrador retrievers jammed into the little trailer, it was an ideal opportunity for Paul to demonstrate his space-saving bed. So with the phonograph going full blast on Paul's latest duck calling record (accompanied by exact—we thought—imitations of his famous high-ball hail call), Paul reached under his bunk and pulled out the flat, briefcase-size package. Always the salesman, Paul unzipped it and shook out the contents. At first glance, there appeared to be more parts than you'd find in a double-doored Swiss cuckoo clock, but Paul soon had the telescoping, "auto-

75

lock," tubular legs and the canvas cover assembled—with only a few parts left over—to the hinges of the "automatic folding" frame.

In fact, "automatic folding" was the first feature Paul demonstrated when he gingerly let down his ample six-foot frame on the cot—with a dramatic sigh of content—as the cot "automatically" and slowly folded up, depositing the demonstrator flat on the floor. Paul lay there on his back, quietly staring up at the ceiling until his black Lab, concerned about his boss' predicament, leaned over and gave him a big, wet kiss.

Undaunted, Paul apologized for his failure "to make a few simple adjustments" and carefully put the cot together again, closely watched by a politely silent, but now widely grinning, audience. Whatever he did on this try seemed to improve the timing because the cot collapsed faster than it did the first time.

Without a word, Paul got up from the floor, turned to the instruction folder, and carefully studied it under the table lamp. Shaking off offers of assistance and all the while quietly humming to himself, he tried it once more. And when the "Easy Carry Canvas Comfy Cot" automatically folded up for the third time, Paul finally exploded. He grabbed the cot, strode to the door, yanked it open, and threw his now field-tested product out into the yard, accompanied by fist shaking and a few remarks yelled into the crisp night wind. Closing the door, he calmly came back in and resumed his duck calling lessons.

The reason we were all crowded into the little trailer for the night was that the old Abraham Lincoln Hotel in the small river town nearby had finally closed down. Much like Paul's cot, it had slowly collapsed, and the weary traveler and tired duck hunter could no longer find rest and solace in this ancient hotel.

With its wavy, warped, and undulating floors, walking down the hallway to your room was much like going down the companionway of a storm-tossed ship. It was easy to be completely sober and still hit both walls before you reached your room.

My first experience as a duck hunting guest at the Abraham Lincoln was unforgettable. Late in the fall and well along toward freeze-up time, I received a last minute phone call at our house in Geneva, Illinois, from my old friend, Hank

Looyer. He invited me to join Paul Stroud, the Anderson boys, Herb Chidley (a well-known wildlife artist), and the rest of the gang for a final duck hunt on the Mississippi . . . leaving in about an hour.

Carefully thinking it over for exactly 10 seconds, I accepted. But now, the problem was my one suit of extra-warm, extra-thick, woolen long underwear. It had just been washed, and clothes dryers had yet to be heard of. So my ever-patient wife, Ruby, wrapped up the still-wet underwear in a big towel and stuffed it into my duffle bag. Better wet than nothing.

Checking in late that night down at the Abraham Lincoln, I immediately confronted the old desk clerk with my problem.

"Nothing to it. Just hang 'em up there over the register. Got a good fire going," he said, pointing to the big, round, hot-air, floor register in the middle of the lobby.

"From the ceiling? Right here in the lobby?" I asked.

"Why not? Hang'em on that light. Right over the register."

So that's what I did. Got a chair and a clothes hanger and hung up my wet, long underwear in the middle of the lobby of the Abraham Lincoln Hotel. And I can tell you now that it certainly dominated the scene. But what I really remember is that no one coming or going through the lobby made any remarks about my underwear or even seemed to notice it. They just ducked or brushed aside the dangling wet legs and kept on going.

Now, I've been in and out of hundreds of hotels and motels since that night. And with all their advertising about "genuine, old-fashioned, heartfelt hospitality and deep concern for the comfort of their patrons," I have yet to see any of their guests' long underwear hung up to dry in the lobby.

And, what's more, I have yet to hear a duck caller as good as Paul Stroud. Even if he did interrupt Hank Looyer and me with our duck calls that night, asking us to sing instead.

After a few sour bars of "Home on the Range," he said, "If you can't sing, you can't blow a duck call. Tomorrow, all I want from you two guys when we are calling those mallards is a single, low-toned quack. Just background—nothing else."

A bitter blow, indeed. Both Hank and I were relegated to the back row of the duck calling chorus. And so, to change that Bible verse a bit—"They also serve who only stand and wait"—I told Hank, "Let's all remember, 'They also serve who only stand and *quack.*'" And "quack" we did . . . all day long.

AFTER ALL HE'S A HOOPER 23

THE Hooper Place had always been as much a part of our town as Old Man Mountain that towered over us. In school, all of us had studied our local history and knew how pioneer Jeremiah Hooper and his family had driven a horse drawn wagon, loaded down with all their worldly goods and leading two cows, over the rough wilderness mountain trail and into this valley in 1795. Jeremiah was truly a remarkable man who won the confidence and friendship of the Indians and was never bothered by them as he, his wife and two husky sons hacked out a farm and built a house. Not a log cabin but a real colonial house that still stands today.

The two sons, taught by Jeremiah and his Indian friends, got to know the ways of the woods and a rifle as well as they knew the plow and the ax. Tales of their marksmanship and hunting prowess became almost legendary, and as I grew up in Green Valley and heard these stories of incredible sharp-shooting and long shots made, they were often followed by an old-timer saying, "No surprise to me. He was a Hooper!"

Over the long years, generations of Hoopers peopled Green Valley and the nearby farms and villages but there was always a Hooper in the Hooper House. The Hoopers were an industrious lot, and the house grew with each generation and finally became a rambling but picturesque old home with white clapboards, green shutters and red brick chimneys.

Like many of my old schoolmates, I left the valley as a young man in the Depression years and went job-hunting over the mountain. Not until long after World War II did I return to Green Valley.

I found it hard to realize what had happened to the sleepy, little mountain that I had left so many years ago. Progress had finally found Green Valley. My first surprise was to find a Burger Hut—with a giant plastic hamburger on the roof— in place of Nick's Olympic Diner, where we had once met on many a frosty fall morning for a sun-up cup of coffee and one of Mrs. Nick's famous homemade doughnuts while our impatient, ready-to-go grouse and woodcock dogs whined and barked in the truck outside.

No more friendly counter stools where you could hook the heels of your hunting boots over the rungs, shoulder-to-shoulder with all the other early risers. Now it was self-service at the computerized cash register and then slide into a dimly lit, Naugahyde-covered "Comfy Corner" with your coffee and a plate of sugared golf balls called "Donut Drops." Evidently, doughnuts with holes had gone out of style in Green Valley.

It was on my first morning that I met Jonathan Jeremiah Hooper himself. It had been years since we had seen each other. Evidently I had changed a bit because when Jonathan stopped at my table he leaned forward and said with a questioning look, "Aren't you Bill Muller?"

"I sure am, Jon," I said and we shook hands. Funny how a man's hands tell you things. Jonathan's grip was still a firm one but his hands seemed thinner and shook a little. Jon had been in high school when I was still in grade school, but our fathers had hunted together and my dad had once kept our two pointers at the Hooper Place. I invited him to join me and as he slid carefully into the seat opposite me I offered him a "Donut Drop."

Absolutely not," he said shaking his head. "I refuse to eat a modern doughnut without a hole. Do they have to change everything?" And then he said sadly, "Sorry, but I guess I'm a dinosaur, left over from another age."

"Me, too," I said. "Especially when it comes to my memories of the old days."

After a long appraising look at me he said, "Heard you were back in town. Meant to call you, but my daugher-in-law is on the phone constantly. A new organization. 'Keep Green Valley Green' or something. 'Too late,' I tell her. 'All the hunting cover is just about gone. Subdivisions and blacktop—everywhere.'" And his voice trailed off.

"You're evidently living in town now," I said. "Who's out at the Hooper Place?"

"The lord of all he surveys. J.C. Blakely himself. God's gift to Green Valley. Owns the new plants here in town. Has his money bailed up in the barn. Impossible old bird. Can't stand him," Jon said bitterly.

"You sold out?" I asked.

"Had to. Too big a price, and the Hooper Farmer's Bank needed it. He's the director now. Owns the house, barn, orchard—and all the woodcock and grouse covers your dad and mine used to hunt together."

"I'd like to see the old place again," I said. Jon hesitated for a moment. "Okay. Tomorrow is Saturday. I'm going up there to see his new colonial house restoration expert. Restoring the whole place. Wants to ask me about an old beehive oven they found in a fireplace. Remember it as a kid. I'll meet you here. Eight o'clock tomorrow morning, okay?"

Jon was late in arriving the next morning but we finally got underway and on the drive up the valley with his old pointer, King, on the back seat, Jon began to work himself up on what he was going to tell J.C. Blakely, and if he thought that Jon was going to ask his majesty if he could hunt those old bird covers up on the hill behind the Place once in a while he could "damn well forget it."

But as things worked out, J.C. himself was sitting on the front steps in his English country tweeds, looking more than a little irritated at our late arrival.

"Good morning, Mr. Hooper," he said. "If there's any of it left." But before Jon could respond, the strangest thing happened. Old King, who I hear usually ignores everyone but Jon and has at one time or other licked every dog in town, jumped over the seat, ran up to the steps where J.C. sat, stuck his cold nose in his face and, so help me, offered his paw.

At first, a red-faced J.C. pushed King away with half a scowl but finally said, "I haven't had a dog greet me like that since I was a kid. My dad had Dan, the best pointer in the state—bar none. Can this old guy hunt?"

"Can he hunt?" Jon said as he got out of the car. "Come hunting season I'll darn well show you."

"It's a date," said J.C. "Come on in, you two guys. Coffee is on the stove."

An hour later as we drove down the mountain Jon had nothing to say. I finally remarked, "That dog of yours is a better judge of character than you are."

"Not so loud. He'll hear you," Jon said. "But let's get out the handtrap for a little practice. I want to show him that an old guy can still shoot. After all, you know, I'm a Hooper."

24 ANDY, THE GREAT GUARD DOG

IT wasn't that Jean Amundsen didn't like dogs, it was just that she wanted them in their proper place. And that proper place was *not* in the house. Raised on a big farm right outside our town here in Green Valley, she was used to the hounds and bird dogs that her dad and three brothers raised. Except for the time when an ailing puppy needed special care and a warm box by the kitchen stove, all the Amundsen dogs stayed outside where they "belonged." Both Jean and her mother saw to that.

Growing up pretty, blonde, and bright with a dazzling smile, it wasn't long before Jean had a yard full of teenage suitors, and the autograph section of her high school yearbook was filled with ardent messages of undying love and devotion from her obviously smitten admirers. With almost all the eligible young males in our small town to pick from, we were somewhat surprised to see that she had chosen Bill Kramer as her partner for the senior prom. Big, plain, slow-moving, smiling Bill was everyone's friend, "But hardly one to set a maiden's heart aflutter," as my wife said.

It wasn't long before we had an invitation to the wedding and a big reception out on the lawn of the Amundsen farm. I still remember Chris Amundsen's vintage elderberry wine, kept special for his only daughter's wedding. "I'll never forget that wine," I say whenever that blessed occasion comes up in conversation. "You certainly *shouldn't!*" my wife says. Chris and I have hunted many a day together.

Later, we heard that the young couple had moved into one of those new houses out on Greenfield Hill and Bill had started traveling for Fairfield Building Supply. Then their

81

daughter, Cindy, was born. But it wasn't until about a year later that I met Bill out on Milford Marsh in his little duck skiff. He pulled up alongside the blind, and we talked. After admiring my old yellow Lab, Belle, he said, "Been reading about them. In Dave Duffey's book, he says a Chesapeake is a one-man or a one-family dog. Not particularly sociable with humans or other dogs . . . and seldom lovable . . . but great retrievers. What do you think?"

"Well, I know they're tough and never quit. Like Mike Cowal's big one—almost 135 pounds. Calls him Bear. Aptly named. Got every dog on the block bluffed. A real fighter. Never leaves Mike's side. Guards Nancy, too, in the house or out."

"I don't know about *in* the house," Bill said and shook his head. "But all the training books say that a dog in the house is easier to train. Get to know each other and all, but a Chesapeake is a pretty big dog and Cindy's awful little and Jean . . ." Bill's voice tailed off and then he brightened up to say, "But that is what I want. A combination guard dog for the house when I'm away and a retriever for me."

"Well, Bill finally got the Chesapeake pup he's been talking about," said Clint Dixon, their next-door neighbor, one morning at the post office. "Out of Mike Cowal's Bear. Named him Andy."

"In or out of the house?" I asked.

"You must have heard about that one," Clint chuckled. "A pretty loud argument, but right now Andy is in the garage."

About mid-September, I met Bill and Andy down at the boat landing. Bill was working a retrieving dummy with the biggest Chesapeake "puppy" I ever saw. Only about four or five months old, he looked like his father—a half-grown "Bear." And he hadn't even started to grow into his enormous feet. No sooner had I gotten out of my car and here he came to greet me, galloping across the parking lot with a welcome jump that almost knocked me down. And with a furiously wagging tail, he kept bumping against my legs, demanding to be petted.

As I stood there scratching his big ears, Bill came over and apologized. "Sorry," he said, shaking his head, "he just wants to be friends with everyone. A great guard dog, too. The garbage man is his favorite."

"Outside of that, how's he doing as a retriever?"

"A natural. Retrieves everything. The kids can't play ball until we tie him up. Keeps retrieving the ball . . . and you ought to see him nail a Frisbee. Catches it on the fly."

"How's he get along with your family?"

"Well, Cindy loves him and they are inseparable in the yard. Andy never leaves her. But with my wife . . . well . . . I guess we can work it out. If only this big mutt would stop lifting his leg on Jean's prize rosebush. Keeps it up no matter how many times she wallops him with her broom. The book says he's marking his home territory. Wish he'd switch to the telephone pole."

"I see that your new neighbor has fenced in his whole yard. And isn't that dog a Doberman pinscher?"

"Yes, and that dog worries me. A mean one. His name is Storm, and he has a fit whenever he sees Andy. Good thing it's a strong fence. And Andy just stands there looking at him and wagging his tail. The great guard dog in action."

The next report I had on Andy was from Clint Dixon, who told me that Jean had finally prevailed and that Andy was now penned up. "Not much of a run, though. Just chicken wire. Looks like he could get out if he really wanted to. Acts like his feelings are hurt. Just sits there and waits for Bill to come home and let him out."

Quite a sight to see them both out duck hunting that fall. In Bill's little skiff with Andy standing up in the bow, it looked like he was paddling a big, happy, brown bear around in the marsh. Hard to figure how he saw around him, and how Andy got out to retrieve and back in without swamping that skiff, I'll still never know.

And then about a week later, it happened. As Clint tells it, "I was out in the yard when I heard Jean scream. Walking up the driveway with an armload of groceries and Cindy toddling behind her . . . and here came that Doberman, head down, hackles up, heading straight for them. Before I could move, Andy came busting right out through the side of his pen all teeth and snarls and met that Doberman head-on. Knocked him flat and sent him home quick. Then I'll be darned if Andy didn't strut up to Jean's rosebush and lift his leg on it again . . . and Jean dropped her groceries and hugged him."

Early the next Saturday morning, I met both Bill and Andy at the landing. Before I could even say hello, Bill reached into his lunch basket in the skiff and tossed me a package of neatly wrapped dog biscuits marked Andy with a note attached that read, "If he gets wet and cold—or even muddy— please bring him in the house. I've got a place all fixed. Have fun, you guys! Love, Jean."

I tossed the package back to Bill, and he said, "How about that? I just found it." Then he fumbled for his handkerchief, blew his nose twice, and then he and the great guard dog, Andy, pushed off into the marsh.

25 WHATEVER HAPPENED TO RUNNING BOARDS

I once heard a wise man say, "Never ask anyone over 51 years old 'How are you doing these days?' unless you've got time to listen to a full report."

So don't ask me, either, or I'll tell you all about my beloved four-wheel-drive wagon that suddenly rusted in half after four years and only 23,000 miles on the beach. Next time, I swear, my truck will get a thorough, freshwater wash down immediately on every return from hunting or fishing on the edge of the sea.

So off we go into the welcoming hands of the smiling car dealers armed with their colorful brochures of roaring, wheel-spinning, turbo-jet wagons bouncing down tortuous trails on the Baja Peninsula. Every truck is pictured in a cloud of flying sand and tumbleweeds with a grim and begoggled daredevil driver gripping the leather-wrapped, shockproof steering wheel. (Tires me out just to look at.) And since I haven't worn racing goggles for some time now, I finally get up

courage enough to ask, "Don't you just have a plain, senior citizen's, 4x4 truck for slow driving on a nice, flat beach at low tide?"

"Right on!" the salesman said. "I've got exactly the model you need. It's the new, multiple-port, SOB Chrome Cruiser, fully loaded up to the computerized glove compartment. Power enough to tow a boxcar loaded with wet cement from here to Kansas City."

And then came the clincher when he proudly showed us a brand-new engineering breakthrough, "optional only on the SOB." "Look," he said, opening the front door, "how easy it is to step up into the captain's chair. Put your foot up on this horizontally streamlined chrome platform, and you're in. We call it the 'come aboard.' "

We call it a "running board," and what in the world ever became of them anyway? Do any of you more mature hunters remember comfortably sitting on it while you put together your take-down pump gun? Or eating your lunch there when you came back to the car at noon? And what a handy place to carry things, out in the open, instantly available. Like extra gasoline in a red can, or extra oil and water in labeled cans held securely by an expanding, black metal rack clamped to the running board. A handy place, too, to carry your dogs in a special running board kennel. And what a sight and sound it was to open up a kennel of little beagles as they spilled out onto the frosty earth with a warm-up series of yips and eager barks. I can hear them now. So here is a notice to Detroit and Tokyo car builders: "The senior hunters of America demand the return of running boards." That ought to get some action!

And then the salesman showed us the new tinted-glass windows. In the old Model T Ford you could sit up high and look around at the passing world as you rattled and rolled along the dusty road. You could wave at your friends and yell down at happy dogs chasing your car. You were in plain sight for all to see. But now with tinted glass, you sit in the back and completely hide from public view. You can look out, but no one can look in. Complete privacy. Do you ever have the feeling that if you stopped one of these tinted-glass cars and looked in the backseat, you might find three hoods wearing ski masks on their way to a bank job?

The reason for this tinted-glass feature, we were told, is to minimize the heat of the sun. Cool and dark. And now we switch our editorial stance and welcome what strides have been made to combat the weather as we drive along with "power-boosted, flow-through ventilation" that keeps us snugly warm in winter and delightfully cool in summer.

When air conditioners were a real novelty, it was a pleasure to hear your passengers complain when you closed the windows and started off on a sticky, hot summer day. Then you proudly switched on your new air conditioner to "high cool," much to their amazement.

It was mid-August many years ago on the North River in Nova Scotia, and my local backwoods guide and I had just come back, sweating and tired, from a long hike upriver looking for Atlantic salmon in the deep pools. Again the miracle of cool air was there in the hot, still woods as I started up my car. The wide-eyed guide, not saying a word, looked hurriedly under the front seat and then in the back before finally crying out, "Aw, come on now! Where's the ice?"

And do any of you remember the "tropicaire" heaters? A gas burner that would instantly fry your kneecaps at the click of a switch when you sat in front, while backseat occupants shivered under blankets. What's more, don't ever put a *wet* duck dog near a "tropicaire." Especially an American water spaniel, whose curly, oily coat, when well heated, gives off fumes that can suddenly stop the car. We had an American water spaniel and a "tropicaire," and rode with all the windows open when the heater was on and Toby was in the car after a long day's hunt.

And then there was my grandfather's story of how they first published road guides for pioneer motorists in Wisconsin. They officially started their mileage charts at the city hall. So, when Granddad started off to northern Wisconsin on a hunting trip, they all had to drive downtown to Milwaukee's city hall in his Overland touring car and set the trip meter at 0. Then 12.8 miles (approximately) north of town on a gravel road it said, "Turn left at the red barn." But if they had repainted the barn brown you were in trouble . . . But somehow they made it, and the hunting was good.

So let's hope that when we hunters put our gear into the car of the future and press the "hunting" button on the computerized "dial-a-destination" before curling up in the optional "bed aboard" backseat, that we will be awakened on arrival by the far-off cries of wild geese, and that the hunting will still be good.

HOW TO EXPLAIN DEER HUNTING TO YOUR LOCAL LIBRARIAN

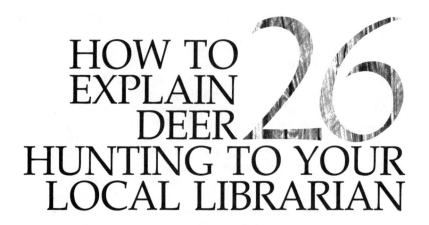

PROLOGUE: *As one deer hunter to another, I can well imagine that you occasionally encounter an anti-hunter, and what may start out as a friendly talk often ends up with the exchange of a few heated words. So you may well recognize what's happening here—in this sort of a play or whatever it is.*

CHARACTERS: JIM, *retired teacher, and* BILL, *retired feed and grain merchant. The same two, old hunting partners in the same Wisconsin town that we met several months ago in what we hope was a lively discussion of the 50th anniversary of the Pittman-Robertson Act, paid for by hunters. The act that brought wildlife back.*

SCENE: *This time we find them both at a neighborhood backyard barbecue. It's fall, and so with glass in hand, they are discussing plans for their annual deer hunt. Miss Alice Anderson, the venerable and outspoken librarian, has been listening. She finally approaches them, and in her best schoolmarm fashion, stamps her foot and says:*

MISS ALICE: Shame on you both! Talking like that about hunting some poor, defenseless creature of the forest. Endangered species, indeed. No wonder! With people like you around.

JIM: [*Smiling and nodding respectfully.*] Well, good afternoon, Miss Alice. That's right. We're both still around. Haven't seen you so wrought up since Bill here stuck me with a pin—right under the "Silence" sign in your library. Didn't really mean to holler out that loud . . . you sure threw us out of there in a hurry. Remember?

BILL: [*Laughing*] I didn't stick you under the "Silence" sign. I stuck you someplace else to wake you up!

MISS ALICE: I well remember you both. Unruly youngsters! And I was young, too. But now you're grown up and still shooting everything in sight. No wonder there are so few deer left. It's you hunters.

BILL: Excuse me, Miss Alice. But there are more deer today in the United States than when Columbus discovered America.

MISS ALICE: Columbus! 1492! How do you know? Were you there?

JIM: No. He was out hunting at the time . . . but seriously. Bill is right. There are now approximately 14 million whitetail deer in this country. For example, right here in the state of Wisconsin we once had a two- or three-month season in 1900, and the hunters took about 2,600 animals. Today we have a nine-day season and the kill, if you'll pardon the word, exceeds 270,000.

MISS ALICE: And every one of them is paraded up the street right by my house, on the tops of cars full of grinning red-coated hunters! Why do you do that? Where everyone can see?

JIM: That's it exactly—where everyone can see. Including the game wardens. It's the law . . . and in more states besides Wisconsin.

BILL: By the way, Miss Alice. How is your brother John doing in Texas? We miss him up at the deer camp.

MISS ALICE: He's doing just fine, thank you. And we haven't heard a thing about his deer hunting, either. Guess he knows how I feel about *that*. And besides, there are probably no deer left in Texas, either, with all those cowboys carrying rifles everywhere.

BILL: Hate to disappoint you, Miss Alice, but what were the figures you had on Texas, Jim?

JIM: Well, according to what I've been reading in your library, Miss Alice, Texas is another example of how the Pittman-Robertson Act has contributed to sound and sensible game management practices that adapt the number of deer to the available range. Records show that there were probably less than 350,000 whitetails in the entire nation in 1900. Loss of habitat and over-hunting had put them on the brink of extinction.

MISS ALICE: Just like the two of you are doing right now.

BILL: [*Starting to slowly simmer.*] Not at all, Miss Alice. Not at all. Jim keeps the figures—while I try to keep my temper, when, begging your pardon, intelligent people like you refuse to recognize simple biological facts. Many of them from your own library. Absolutely refuse to!

JIM: Okay, Bill, calm down or you'll have to stay after school. Now, back to a few more facts and Texas, which alone has more than 10 times the number of whitetails (4.2 million of them) than existed in the entire nation 80 years ago.

MISS ALICE: Well, these are quite interesting figures. But now that you say you have restored all the deer, why don't you just leave them alone so people can enjoy them? Protect the poor things. Stop hunting.

BILL: There we go again! Because without hunting there would be more deer than food to feed them and places to live. Would you like to see them all weak and starving with packs of wild dogs and coyotes pulling them down? Is that what you want?

JIM: Bill, I'm afraid, is getting a little upset, Miss Alice. But he's right. The nation's herds would double almost over-night, and millions of deer would die of starvation.

MISS ALICE: Then why do some of those national organi-zations oppose hunting—of any kind?

JIM: Because they are being ruled by their emotions rather than their intellects.

BILL: That's right. Show me one professionally and academ-ically trained wildlife manager who is opposed to hunting, and I'll hang up my rifle.

MISS ALICE: Very interesting. Somewhat biased, but inter-esting. And if you two are doing any more research in my library, remember—no pins! [*She laughs and rejoins the crowd.*]

JIM: I wonder if we won that one?

BILL: Who knows? But at least we tried.

27 COUNT YOUR STEPS, BOY, COUNT YOUR STEPS

I F you have been faithfully reading and trying to follow the recommendations of hunting experts in magazines and books as many years as I have, and have retained only a small fraction of these tips, hints, hunches, and shortcuts to success, you'll literally be awash with advice. No matter what the hunting problem or challenge of the chase, you'll be prepared. If it's how to cape out a trophy mountain goat or remove a porcupine quill from the seat of your pants, you'll be ready, my friend, you'll be ready.

For some reason or other I have never felt that I knew enough to be considered an expert on anything, with the possible exception of jugging for catfish (and there doesn't seem to be much call for that these days). On the other hand, I somehow feel compelled to ask myself, *Haven't you learned anything valuable about hunting after all these years? Something must have stuck.*

Thinking back I'll bet many of you will agree that what really stuck, hard and fast, is what we learned from our dad, grandad, uncle, or whoever first took us hunting as a wide-eyed, eager kid. We learned because we wanted to be accepted, so we listened to our elders with an intensity that, if applied to our schoolwork, would have made us all honor students. And as a young and too often truant rebel who packed four years of high school into *five*, I speak with some authority.

Safe gun handling was my first lesson, boiled down into one sharp and often loud command, "Watch that muzzle!" or "Don't just tell me your gun is empty—show me!" And when I forgot, trailing far behind the hunting party in full disgrace with an unloaded gun was the indelible penalty. Especially when the birds got up and all I could do when

91

they came back over me was point at them with my empty gun.

Hitting what I shot at was the second lesson. I had taught myself the principles of leading a target with the help of a garden hose and the neighbors' running cat, but it was in the duck blind that I listened to my dad. As a world-champion shotgunner, shooting was his business, so I listened—man, how I listened. And I learned to sit "still as a bump on a log," keeping my eager face down, no barrel waving and head twisting. Peering out from under my cap, rolling my eyeballs till they ached, I would watch the birds working to Dad's call. And then on Dad's "okay" I learned to move all in one smooth motion, raising the gun to my shoulder as I stood and swinging it all in the same smooth sweep ahead of the bird.

What's more, as the experts say, you can practice this "rise and swing" sweep by getting up from a chair on the front porch. If the neighbors wonder what you're shooting at and threaten to call the police, retreat ·to the parlor, but watch out for your wife's new table lamp. (I still practice this smooth swing, but lately it doesn't help very much. Could it be these new glasses?)

More shotgun shooting practice advice, often repeated, was, "Don't forget, wood to wood." Translated, it means, "Keep your *wooden* head tight to the *wooden* stock. Don't peek. Don't raise your head. It's wood to wood—and keep your eye on the target. Nothing else. Shut out the world. Just that target."

"Instinct shooting" I guess they call it now. I once saw the famous teacher of instinct shooting, Lucky McDaniels, prove it once and for all by tossing a BB up in the air and hitting it with *another* BB from his air rifle. So help me.

Over the years I have finally learned a few things about reading a map and compass, deer hunting in the north woods, and knowing where camp should be at the end of the day (although it often seems to wander off aimlessly where it shouldn't be). The simplest advice on finding camp I ever got was from my dad. "I don't want you in the woods without an ax on your belt . . . and when all else fails and there's snow on the ground, turn around and backtrack like hell while it's still light. And if it looks like dark is coming fast, stop while you can see, look for a pitch-pine stump, and tear into it with your axe. Then start the biggest fire you

can, sit down, and stay there . . . it'll warm you up. If there's
no snow, build the same kind of fire and stay put. Don't
look for us—we'll come find you." A short course in survival.

As for the fundamentals of direction, my grandad Mitchell
said to me one day, as I was sitting on the porch at Pine
Lake admiring my shiny compass, "Boy, if you leave the
road heading northwest which way do you go when you
want to come back?"

Looking at my compass I said proudly, "Southeast, sir."

"And don't you forget it!" Grandad said. And I haven't.

I don't believe I've seen the following bit of advice in the
outdoor magazines, where everyone seems to be keen, lean,
young, muscular, tough, and durable, regardless of the
weather, depth of the snow, or the altitude. Right out of the
office one fall, where my daily exercise was a brisk walk to
the coffee machine and back, I found myself up to my knees
in the relentless, clinging mud of a South Dakota duck marsh.
Leaving the blind with Dad, I was carrying a sack of heavy
wooden decoys in one hand, a limit of fat mallards over my
back, and my old Remington Model 11 humpback autoloader
(it weighed at least 36 pounds) in the other. With only 100
yards to the road, I was starting to flounder and thrash about
a bit when Dad, who was behind me with two heavy boat
boxes and his gun called out, "Count your steps and rest,
boy. Count your steps."

Good idea, I thought. I'll try 25 steps. I made it to 18, and
puffing like a beached whale, I stopped. Then 14 and a rest.
Finally after the next 12 steps, I sat down on the sack of
decoys. Back to counting steps. Easy does it. Keep counting.
Stop. Count again. Pretty soon we were both back on the
road, high and dry.

Thirty years later, it was time to count again. I had left our
high camp in the thin air of Nepal's lofty Himalaya Mountains—highest in the world—to foolishly follow a big, colorful
Impeyan pheasant (it was as big as a turkey) down the side
of a mountain trail. No trouble going down, and only 100
yards to come back up. The camp bell rang for supper, and
as I started back up the trail, I realized, a little too late, that
our expedition leader's altimeter had just registered 14,200
feet. Twenty feet back up, my knees started to tremble and
my heart started to pound. Standing there, catching my
breath and a little scared, I clearly heard Dad say, "Count
your steps, boy, count your steps."

28 A STRANGE EVENT ON GREENHEAD BOULEVARD

COMING out of the dark, he found himself on a wide and empty street he had never seen before . . . marked "Greeenhead Boulevard." As he made his way in silent wonder along the brightly lit street, he suddenly saw a large, imposing building at the head of the boulevard. Across the tall, white pillars stretched a sign that read in dignified script, "The Academy of Waterfowl Deception."

Drawn by some compelling, mysterious power, he hurried, in a half-run, down Greenhead Boulevard to the Academy. As he finally stood breathless at the foot of the marble steps, a tall, lean, gray-bearded figure in a full, flowing, camouflage cape and a long-peaked, camouflage duck hunting cap came out through the huge bronze doors of the building and moved slowly down the steps to meet him.

"We've been waiting for you, John," the figure said in a strange voice that rose and fell like the call of far-off geese.

"For me?" asked John in an awed whisper.

"Yes," the old man said and, like the Ancient Mariner, fixed him "with his glittering eye" as he seized John's arm in a viselike grip. "We've heard about your calling problems, but now you have found us. Your troubles are over."

"Excuse me, but who are you and what do I do?" John asked, still wide-eyed.

"I, sir, am Professor Humbert Q. Hailcall at your service. Executive Director of the Academy of Waterfowl Deception and Master of the Quackenflopper Duck and Goose Calling System. And you are invited to join us."

"The Quackenflopper System?"

"Yes. A closely guarded secret family formula—my mother was a Quackenflopper. The system developed during the Middle Ages in the marshes of Goosesylvania and was handed down from one generation to another. The inventor, Quidley

95

Q. Quackenflopper, blessed be his name, was Royal Caller to the King of Goosesylvania."

"Never heard of Goosesylvania," John said a bit puzzled.

"Of course not. They had to change its name in the 16th century to protect it from the barbaric hordes of hunters invading it from the North."

"Why were they called barbarians?"

"Because they shot birds on the water and littered the marshes with sausage rinds and broken beer mugs."

"Say, this whole thing is beginning to sound like a dream," said John, slowly shifting his gaze from the professor up the marble steps of the academy building looming white and silent above them.

"It *is* a dream, John. A dream come true for you. Once you have mastered the system, you no longer need to suffer the insults of your fellow hunters. Wasn't it George Kirschke who said you could make a fortune with your call driving the ducks off the rice crops in Louisiana?"

"I'm afraid so. That smart aleck, Kirschke! But now I've got my new duck calling cassette, and I practice every night."

"We know, John, we know. There has been a rumor in your neighborhood that you are keeping a hyena in your house and are mistreating it."

"That's Kirschke again. Well, okay. What's the cost?"

"You're in luck, John. We have a special offer this month a mere $62,000. Payable, of course, in one easy lump sum."

"That seems a little high, professor. Any guarantees? What if—if you'll pardon the expression—the course isn't what it's quacked up to be?" asked John, beginning to enjoy the negotiations. "And just what will you teach me?"

"We will teach you to use the Quackenflopper Call, which will enable you to honk like a Canada goose, 'tootle' like a whitefront, 'whonk' like a snow or blue, and 'kurr-onk' like a brant. Once the geese are mastered, we move over to ducks, and you will learn to quack like a mallard, whistle like a pintail, squeal like a wood duck, growl like a canvasback, 'meow' like a redhead, and 'purr' like a scaup—just to mention a few," said the professor, finally pausing for a breath.

"All that with one call?" John asked in amazement.

"Yes, the Quackenflopper Call. Lifetime maintenance service. We change the oil every six months and adjust the reticules. And as for a guarantee, we have never had a complaint. But if you're not fully satisfied, we will refund your money—and you can keep the hard hat and the gun with our compliments."

"Hard hat and gun?" John asked.

"Yes. Safety rules require you wear a camouflage hard hat when using the call. Protects your head from the beaks of excited ducks and geese that may dive into the blind."

"You must be kidding," John said quietly. "And the gun?"

"A new Federal Migratory Waterfowl ruling. We are allowed to shoot only a single-shot 410 when operating the call. Applies to the other hunters in the blind as well."

"Okay, okay, I'm sold," John said as he scribbled out a check and handed it to the professor. "When do I start?"

"Please, John. One thing at a time. We require, merely as a formality of course, that you take our entrance examination. Helps us determine your current level of proficiency, something on which we can build. Do you have your call?"

"Of course. Carry it with me at all times," John said, fumbling in his pocket.

"Fine. Now if you don't mind, I'd like to hear you run through the basic quack, a hail call, and a chuckle or two," the professor said with a friendly smile. Whereupon John drew himself up, filled his lungs, and started to call. Halfway through his performance, the professor suddenly raised a long, skinny arm in the air, slowly shook his gray-bearded head, and with a solemn bow, returned the check. While John stood in stunned silence, the professor turned, ascended the broad steps, and disappeared through the big doors. Not until the bronze doors shut with a hollow clank did John fully realize that he had just failed the entrance examination to the Academy of Waterfowl Deception.

Looking about in bewilderment, he ran up the steps and beat his fists on the closed doors, crying out, "Wait! Wait! One more call. Listen to my come-back call," as he started blowing again.

"John, wake up! You're quacking like a duck. I told you not to play that cassette before you went to bed. Wake up."

"What? What?" John asked, sitting up in the bed. "Where have I been?" He shook his head and then asked, "Mary, do you know of a street called Greenhead Boulevard?"

"No. And neither do you. You've been dreaming."

"Guess so. But I could look it up in the Yellow Pages."

"Stop your mumbling and go to sleep. Good night, John."

"Good night, professor—I mean, dear."

UP TO HIS ARM-PITS IN CEDAR SWAMP 29

OVER the years, I've noticed that when someone proudly says, "Well, one thing I've got is a good sense of humor," chances are, they haven't. Humor is such an elusive quality that psychologists are still arguing about an adequate definition.

I'm pretty sure, however, that styles of humor often change with the times. The broad practical joke that was considered funny many years ago in this country of ours is an outmoded example. "Frontier humor" the professors called it, and it rarely needed an explanation.

I can well remember my dad's stories about the little logging town of Amasa in the Upper Peninsula of Michigan where the Mitchell family spent their summers camping, hunting, and fishing along the Net River. It was in the early 1900s, and the Chicago, Milwaukee, and St. Paul railroad had just penetrated that wilderness.

The Mitchells got to know and admire the colorful characters of the region, and the names of woodsmen like George Primo and Billy Robinson became familiar to all of us who heard my grandfather's and my father's stories.

Whitetail deer were plentiful in this region, and the new railroad began to draw hunters from cities like Chicago. Guiding was a relatively new occupation, but when you got paid hard cash for going hunting, it soon caught on around Amasa. Evidently, though, the problem of social relationship between the "sport" and his guide wasn't immediately resolved. This was still frontier America, and *no one* doffed his cap to any man unless he chose to.

And then one fine September day, as my dad told it, a Mr.

Charles Kingsley, Chicago industrialist, stepped off the afternoon train. He had wired ahead to Amasa for three guides, and Billy Robinson was one of them. They had expected three hunters, but only Mr. Charles Kingsley, his trunk, two duffle bags, and four cased rifles arrived. Things immediately got off to the wrong start when their new sport brushed aside the ritual of outstretched hands and introductions and began giving orders for the disposition of his luggage together with sharp admonitions about the careful handling of his four rifles. Carrying nothing himself, Mr. Kingsley led the heavily laden and somewhat sheepish safari up the main street to the hotel.

I can't quite remember all the details, but I do recall that Mr. Kingsley ignored the usual welcoming drink in the hotel bar with his staff of guides and had a single whiskey and soda sent up to his room. Things got no better when he came down to dinner that evening and sat alone in solemn and regal splendor.

Mr. Kingsley's "staff" by this time was beginning to take a bit of kidding, and their attitudes hovered between irritation and amusement. They had never been treated this way before, but he had paid in advance, so they took Mr. Kingsley hunting early the next morning—out on the tote road north of town and along the edge of Big Cedar Swamp. Three guides and one sport. As Billy Robinson said, "He was well guided."

The guides set up a short drive and, as luck would have it, Mr. Kingsley downed a splendid buck with one shot. Billy said, "He actually smiled. Got out a tape measure and began measuring the horns. Something about fellows named Boone and Crockett. I thought they was both dead."

"Somehow, we never did get around to shaking his hand," Billy continued. "Then he began giving orders on how to dress out that big buck—like we'd never done it before—and how to tie the rope and how to haul him out. Military orders, sort of. By this time, the other two guides, Jim and Bob, were looking a little tight-lipped and glum, but we went along with him. And then, by gosh, if Mr. Kingsley didn't take over on the way back to town. He decided to go right across Big Cedar Swamp instead of going back the way we came in. I told him—stepping from root to root—that there were some deep holes in the bog, but he said his 'woodsman's instinct' told him it was the shortest route and that he planned to catch the noon train. So off he went, leading the way.

"Well, we hadn't gone more than thirty rod when our leader slipped off a root and went into the bog up to his armpits. This didn't even faze Mr. Kingsley. He just kept saying 'All right, men. Hurry up and get me out of here. A needless delay.' The three of us just stood there and looked at our employer stuck tight in the bog. We all must have had the same idea because with a few winks, we laid down our rifles and made believe we were trying to get him out. One of us would pull up on one arm while the other pushed down on the other arm with a lot of loud heaving and grunting—and instructions from Mr. Kingsley.

"Finally, we gave up and stepped back to judge the situation. 'Well,' I said, 'what do you think?' Jim and Bob just shook their heads and looked sad. 'Can't just leave him here for a bobcat or wolf to get him,' I continued. 'Hate to do it, but it looks like we'll have to shoot him.' 'No other way,' Jim and Bob agreed.

"This talk really shut up Mr. Kingsley. He just stared up at us. So with a big sigh, I made a fuss about working the lever on my Winchester .30—30 when Mr. Kingsley passed out cold.

"Well, we all took to laughing and pulled him up out of the bog with one big heave just as he came to. The he picked up his rifle and, without a word, went hopping straight across the swamp, trailing mud and water. We never saw him again. He just got mad and went home. We had to eat his deer, too. The horns are still up over the hotel bar.

"A peculiar man, Mr. Kingsley. He should have known I wouldn't have shot him. Hell, I hardly knew the man."

30 TOODLES– THE RETRIEVING POODLE

IN the best of literary tradition, a writing man of my years is supposed to stare into the flickering flames of a cozy hearth, with faithful dog asleep underfoot, and in these flames live once again glorious memories of a hunting past. And then record these meditations in undying prose.

But it doesn't work out that way at all with me. Cozy hearth, indeed. It's cozy, all right, and the new Vermont Casting Stove with the open fireplace front works well in winter here on the Outer Banks of North Carolina, where your garbage cans blow away never to be seen again. (I'm thinking of a banding program to determine where they really go.) Very cozy, but somehow we manage to put the stovepipe in upside down so that bubbling, black creosote from the burning wood leaks down the outside of the pipe, dripping onto the polished stove and the cozy hearth below. Not much time for meditation when you're busy mopping up. (Yes, I do plan to reverse the nesting of the long, black pipe, I tell my wife, Ruby. But it's summertime now, and maybe I'm like the man with the leaky roof. When it wasn't raining, he didn't need a patch, and when it rained, how could he possibly make a good repair?)

As for the sleeping dog, it's a puppy that never sleeps and loves to gnaw—in spite of a wallop—on the rungs of my new fireside chair. So when do I do my meditative recall of my hunting past? Easy. I do it when the fishing is slow; I put my rod in the sand spike and sprawl out in the sun on South Beach.

And suddenly there I am, backwards in time. Gun in arm and asleep beneath another sun in a high grass pocket on a hillside near the shore of Bitter Lake in Day County, South Dakota. Duck hunting country full of sloughs, marshes, and lakes. A noontime lull in the flight, and since I was up early that morning sitting on the steps of the old clubhouse waiting for Walter North, part-time guide and house painter, to pick me up, I can use a nap.

That was the morning I had looked across the endless Dakota prairie to see the first faint colors of the rising sun and a wisp of ducks moving across the eastern sky. I was young then and not much on philosophical musing, but somehow I knew. I was really back in South Dakota, chock full of the feeling of being alive.

Then I heard a loud noise far off on the prairie. Like someone towing a bag of broken dishes and a big piece of galvanized tin roofing. I knew it was Walter's Model T sedan long before I saw it. Accustomed as we all are to the quiet hum of a modern car in motion, it's hard to remember how much noise an old "well-broken-in" Model T Ford could make as it bumped along, twisting and turning over rutted, muddy roads.

Eventually making it into the yard, Walter, shaking and shivering to a stop, yelled over the roar of his sedan, "Come on, kid, let's go." As I approached the car, he said, "Watch the door. I've been adjusting it."

And so he had. Tightly closed with a piece of baling wire, the one-piece repair kit carried by all Model T owners. My dad used to say, "Without baling wire, a Model T will two-bit you to death!"

As I unwound the wire and reached in to put my gun on the back seat, a shaggy, little white dog appeared from the corner and gave me a nasal, teeth-baring snarl.

"Don't mind her," Walter yelled as we started off. "She only bites a little!"

"What *is* it?" I yelled back.

"Her name is Toodles. Mostly poodle, spitz, and a little Pekingese. Belongs to my mother-in-law. Borrowed her for the day. She doesn't exactly know I have her. Best retriever you ever saw."

"Retriever?" I shouted. "Meadowlarks?"

"Nope. Ducks. Don't she look like a retriever to you?"

Walter laughed and gave the wheel a jerk, narrowly missing

a big cock pheasant that ran up out of the ditch and across the road. In a country that was then so full of pheasants, no mention of the near miss was made. No more than if a crow had flown by.

When we finally rattled up to the south shore of Bitter Lake and shut off the engine to a deafening silence, we could see a big raft of waterfowl resting on the shallow reaches in the distance. Mostly mallards, the binoculars said, with a sprinkling of canvasbacks, redheads, and bluebills. As we watched, several big bunches of bluebills strung across the water took off and swung to the north, then turned and started back toward the hill above us. Walter had parked his faithful car alongside a flat patch of mud sunbaked into geometric patterns. But below the crust, waiting for your careless foot, were five inches of black, sticky gumbo mud— one of nature's most effective and tenacious adhesives.

Skirting the gumbo flat with Walter carrying a panting, eager Toodles under one arm to avoid staining her coat with mud, we climbed the hill. And what a shoot it was. Toodles worked like a Lab dragging the chunky bluebills back to Walter only (she snapped at me when I tried to receive one). And then, of course, we dropped a duck out in the mud, and Toodles, covered from muzzle to tip of tail with black gumbo ooze, retrieved it. Now I was waiting patiently for Walter, who in a state of panic for fear of his mother-in-law, had taken the little dog down to the alkaline lake to try to clean her up.

Suddenly the wet, cold nose of Karina, Marcia Lyons' well-known Chesapeake/Lab retriever, was in my ear, and I awakened on South Beach with Marcia standing above me saying, "Sorry, Jack, but Ruby asked me to ask you when you are going to fix that pipe on the woodstove."

Meditation, indeed.

WEIRD AND WONDERFUL 31

AS one hunter-fisherman type to another, have you ever had the impulse to write to a company whose general ad shows a photographer's "model" outdoorsman happily fishing in a bass and bluegill pond using a deep sea trolling rod with the reel on upside down? Or how about a keen-eyed "studio" duck hunter crouching in a camouflaged blind wearing a blaze-orange cap visible at 7½ miles? Of course you have. But do we do anything about it? Hardly ever.

But, in this case, enough is enough. I have just been reading *Encyclopedia Brown's Record of Weird and Wonderful Facts* by Donald J. Sobel. It's packed full of fascinating and completely useless information, like "fingernails grow a fifth faster in summer than they do in winter, and twice as fast during the day as at night." (A fact you can always use during an awkward lull in the conversation.) Or did you know that, "All the people in the world would fit into a box a mile high by a mile wide by a mile long and the box would fit easily into the Grand Canyon?"

And so it went, reading along with *Encyclopedia Brown* until I was brought up short with a long list of, "The underdog, the bonehead, the innocent victim, the unlucky Harry. His moment of fame has too long been overlooked." The sad tale of Phillip Brown, who changed jobs after 17 years with the Royal Society for the Protection of Birds. In 1966 he became editor of *Shooting Times*, an English hunting magazine.

The casual assumption that someone who has worked 17 years for a bird protection society should suddenly become an editor of a hunting magazine automatically becomes a "weird and wonderful fact." It is so typical of the general public's attitude toward hunting and the hunter that I see a little red. How long do we have to put up with the woefully mistaken ideas that the hunter is somehow the sworn enemy of all wildlife?

And now that we are "how longing," how long do we have to put up with the idea that someone who knows enough about birds to tell an ostrich from a woodpecker is some kind of nut? "Seen any double-breasted, seer-suckers lately?" is the usual greeting that a known bird watcher—hunter or no—gets from some grinning muscle-head who hasn't been outside his home since one of his Christmas cigars set off the smoke alarm. If you said you were an "animal watcher" and spent hours sneaking up on unsuspecting otters and short-tailed shrews, it would somehow be all right. But just mention bird watching to most people and you have joined the lunatic fringe of society, classed with little old ladies in sneakers, absent-minded professors, or worse, limp-wristed esthetes.

Be it bird watching or a similar form of nature study, if you are big enough and sensitive enough, you can react physically to the ignorant sneers of your peers. Well do I remember George Gross, Phi Delta Theta fraternity brother and duck hunter friend of mine at the University of Wisconsin. George was a deceptively mild, quiet, polite, outwardly plump and somewhat rotund agriculture major. One of his courses at the "ag" school was ornithology (the study of birds), and it was necessary for George to photograph and study a prescribed number of local birds.

Armed with his camera one sunny fall morning, he started up Bascom Hill to start his collection. In full lumbering pursuit of a red-breasted robin, frolicking like a black bear, he was suddenly interrupted by a wolf whistle and, "Yoo, hoo, fatty! Take a few pix for me!" Stopping abruptly, George located two husky, grinning spectators waving their handkerchiefs at him from the sidewalk. George carefully left his camera underneath a tree and slowly went over to address his distractors. The result? Two varsity football players failed to show up for practice that afternoon. They were being held in the school infirmary for further observation.

My interest in birds as a young hunter was separated into two classes—edible and non-edible; game and non-game. Although my dad could tell a flying hen mallard from a gadwall at 200 yards, as well as a hairy from a downy woodpecker in the top of the tallest tree, my sole interests were game birds. Completely edible, huntable, sensible game. Anything else, known to many so-called outdoorsmen as tweety birds and game-killing hawks and owls, were ignored. 107

And then a beautiful girl, who became my wife, Ruby, appeared on the scene. Early in our courtship during a day on the Yellowstone River in her home state of Montana, a lone hawk sailed above us in a slow circle. "Look at that big chicken hawk," I said wisely, in all my outdoor knowledge.

"Chicken hawk?" she said in some disgust. "You're a big fake. If you can't shoot it and eat it, you don't know what it is. That's a Swainson's hawk. Don't you see its dark terminal tail band? And they don't eat chickens—they eat gophers, rats, and grasshoppers."

And it wasn't because I didn't want to argue with this wonderful girl for fear of offending her. And it wasn't—Lord forbid—that I didn't like arguments. It was because for once in my life, I couldn't think of an answer. So all I said was, "I think you're right. Maybe it's time I started learning about all kinds of birds."

So learn we did, and the outdoors became just that much more enjoyable. I leaned towards hawks and owls, but Ruby's field was broader. In fact, years later when we were in the midst of a group of confirmed, lifelong, bird-watching enthusiasts (no more confirmed or enthusiastic, incidentally, than a group of old hunters) one of the group asked, "Ruby, what's your favorite bird?" After a thoughtful pause, Ruby answered, "Fried chicken." But she didn't really mean it. If pressed she'll vote for the great, black-backed gull, that big, serious, dignified predator with its $5\frac{1}{2}$-foot wingspan. A study of dazzling black and white, they flock here to Hatteras Island, North Carolina, by the thousands in the winter time, and slowly flap away before our wagon as we drive the windswept beach. Duck hunters hurry to make a quick retrieve on a floating duck if there's a black-back around, before that big, robber gull leaves nothing but feathers and a few bones.

Now, I don't really expect you readers to rush right out and buy a bird book to start your own list of birds—game and non-game—seen and identified. But if you do this in an attempt to raise your outdoor IQ, and someone kids you, please get their names and addresses so I can turn them over to George Gross. On a more serious note, *Encyclopedia Brown* says, "You breathe about 10 million times a year." So don't stop and be sure to have a Merry Christmas. "Best wishes from everyone in our house to everyone in yours."

32 UNCLE BILL AND THE HOLLYHOCKS

"**W**HAT can I do for you, Bud?" Uncle Bill asked as he stopped his rocking chair in the forward position in order to clear the porch railing with a stream of tobacco juice expertly aimed into the tall hollyhocks. "Keeps the beetles off," he said, as his teenage nephew came up onto the porch with a clipboard and pencil in hand.

"Well, I've got this assignment in English to write about deer hunting," Bud said as he perched up on the railing. "And since you've been guiding those city hunters all these years, I figured maybe you could help me, Uncle Bill. Could you do that? Please."

"You know, I should be weeding that darn garden for your Aunt Mary . . . but go ahead. What do you want to know?" Uncle Bill asked, resuming his rocking.

"That new teacher said I should list a lot of tips for hunting the whitetail deer and give specific examples of each thing you should do," Bud said, reading from his clipboard.

"Be simpler to list the things you *shouldn't* do. A list of 'don't's' maybe instead of a list of 'do's.' "

"Okay with me," Bud answered, getting a firm grip on the clipboard. "Let's go. Now what's the first 'don't' for those deer hunters?"

"Don't rush me—that's one of the 'don't's.' Let me think now," Uncle Bill said as he stopped rocking and stared up over Bud's head at a lone red-tailed hawk circling high in the clear September sky.

" 'Don't number one,' " he finally said. "Don't come up to my place to practice rifle shooting. I run a deer camp, not a rifle range. Sight-in your rifle back home. It's okay to fire a few test shots to see if you're still sighted-in, but not to practice, for the love of Mike. When I was back in town one year, one guy shot up three boxes of .30-06 ammo in camp 109 the day before the season opened. Even the bluejays left the woods for the next few days."

"Okay, I got it," said Bud, scribbling busily. "What's next?"

"Don't overdo that new deer scent business. Take it easy. Fellow from Pittsburgh got carried away with the idea of smelling like a deer. Just open up a window, and you could smell him miles away heading back to camp. Heard he tried it down in Georgia, and the hounds they were using actually put him up a tree. Thought they had a two-legged deer," Bill said, smiling and shaking his head.

"Another 'don't' you should list is about rattling those antlers. Works pretty good sometimes, but don't sit there for hours at a time constantly rattling and scraping those horns together. I know it's supposed to imitate two bucks in the rut having a fight—but not *all day*. Even John L. Sullivan and Jake Kilrain, in that long, bare-knuckle championship fight they had back in the 90s, gave up after 71 rounds."

Bud stopped writing, looked up and asked, "John L. who?"

"John L. Sullivan. The greatest fighter who ever lived. Don't they teach you anything in that school you go to!" Uncle Bill answered in a shocked tone.

After a brief pause, Bill regained his composure and continued. "Same goes for that deer call. Don't overdo it. I've never seen a doe go around all day blatting its head off. Like the old hair cream slogan, 'a little dab will do you.' And that might well apply to deer scent, too.

"Next, Don't get lost . . . please! Most deer hunters carry a good, reliable compass, but knowing where you are ain't worth a damn unless you know in what direction camp is or where you left your car. Look at your compass and carry a map when you leave the road, and remember your course. Simplest thing in the world to remember is, 'If you're going into the woods heading on a north-by-west course, you've got to go south by east to come back.' Yet, last fall one of those computer scientists—guess you could call him—couldn't figure out his compass. Too simple, I guess. Nicest kind of fellow but he got lost twice going to the outhouse.

"If you do get lost and there's snow on the ground, but no snow coming down, backtrack, man, backtrack. Above all, don't panic. Sit down, think it over, and build a fire. If you hear three shots, answer back. But stay put. Don't wander all over hell and gone looking for us. We'll come to you, so stay where you are and keep the fire going."

"Not so fast, please," Bud pleaded, writing at full speed. "Okay, next point."

"An important one, too. Don't be a noisy still-hunter. If you are going to be a still-hunter, be *still*. Go as quiet as you can—every step.

"Not like the time I met that big fat guy from over at Kenny Waite's camp. I was up north on the old fire lane when I heard this noise coming up that long ridge to the south. Sounded like an organized deer drive with all kinds of brush cracking, rattling, thumping, clanging, and floundering in that heavy cover until I realized it was not a bunch of hunters on a drive but only *one* lone hunter. I could hear him puffing and coughing as he came nearer, and with one headlong rush through the bull briars and underbrush, he finally staggered up onto the fire lane, rifle in hand, right smack in front of me. Sweating a steady stream in a big, hunter-orange parka of hard, shiny plastic with cap and pants to match— guaranteed to be noisy in the brush—he looked like a barrel on fire. With his parka belted at the waist with a hunting knife big enough to dress out a bull elephant together with a noisy tin cup hooked on a metal clip and a bag of loose, jingling cartridges in hand, he took a big cigar out of his mouth, coughed a few times, and said, 'Hope I didn't startle you *sneaking* up on you like this. It's these things I wear,' he continued, pointing down at a big pair of genuine beaded buckskin moccasins. 'Indians wear them still-hunting. Sneak right up on a deer without a sound.' Before I could think of anything to say, he coughed some more, put his cigar back in place, waved goodbye, and crashed back into the brush heading north—*still-hunting* all the way."

"I'm running out of space," Bud said, writing furiously. "How many more 'don't's' have you got?"

"Dozens of 'em!" Uncle Bill said with some irritation. "Don't you want to hear about 'Don't forget to bring your Tums to camp when I'm doing the cooking,' or 'Don't move off a deer stand when I put you there . . . or I'll break your neck.' "

"Not enough room," Bud answered. And after a pause, he said seriously, "Honestly now, Uncle Bill, aren't you exaggerating a little bit to make these 'don't's' seem stronger?"

"Could be, Bud. Could be," Uncle Bill said softly as he looked up over Bud's head, smiled at the redtail still circling high in the sky, made another application of bug-killing juice to the hollyhocks, and then went back to some serious rocking.   111

Harry Floyd Joecke

33 A DARK DAY ON ROCKWELL MOUNTAIN

IT was one of those strangely quiet, dark, windless days on the mountain. I hadn't seen the sun since early morning, and then only for a short time after I left camp to climb up Rockwell Mountain and spend the last day of the season alone on my favorite deer stand overlooking Bull Valley.

Climbing, I caught a few old deer tracks in the snow but no signs of other hunters. It looked as if I just might have the entire mountain to myself for the day. Puffing a little bit, I finally reached the stand. Brushing the snow off my favorite flat rock, I carefully sat down, sort of wiggled around until I found what seemed like a softer spot, and then relaxed against the base of the ancient white pine behind me. And there it was at my feet, the whole blessed length of Bull Valley. Still wild, still almost untouched.

Sliding off my right glove in the snug slash pocket of my jacket, I felt for my friendly hand warmer, and then I opened the bolt of my rifle to check the waiting .30-06 cartridge. All was well, so I closed the smoothly running bolt with a satisfying metallic *click* and then sighted through my new riflescope, which brightened up the dark day in a way that continued to please and amaze me. Now if I could just put those meticulously tapered crosshairs on the shoulder of a good buck.

The check-out completed, I put my insulated hunting glove back on and snuggled down a little bit more in the padded parka hood of my blaze-orange, down-filled jacket. With warm hands and warm feet in my insulated hunting boots, I silently praised the gifts and glories of the Plastic Age that comforted me in the years of my advancing age as a deer hunter. And so I settled down to wait for a possible shot.

I must have settled down a little too far because I was suddenly awakened from my short nap by a flutter of wings in the pine directly above me. Looking down at me with a

113

beady black eye, an inquisitive blue jay cocked his crest and emitted a surprisingly low, musical note. But when I raised my head to say "hello," he let out a typical, harsh cry of alarm that sounded like, "Look out, look out, jay, jay, jay!"

"Shut up, you blue-feathered, egg-stealing pest," I yelled.

"Aye," said a voice directly behind me. "He is that, all right. And now he's told every deer on this mountain exactly where we are."

Turning my head to the right, I saw a pair of buckskin moccasins and the stock of a muzzleloading rifle with its curved brass buttplate. As my eyes traveled up and behind me, I saw what was apparently a real muzzleloading fan dressed to the hilt—fringed buckskin, coonskin cap, beard and all. He looked strangely authentic as he stood there smiling down at me.

"Hi," I said. "I didn't know the primitive firearm season was still open."

"Primitive?" he said, looking down with a puzzled frown at his long-barreled rifle. "It's one of Riley Rogers' newest percussion locks. Got it over at The Gulph 'bout a month 'fore I went away."

"Where did you go?" I asked.

"Don't really know. Away somewhere. Probably for a long time. Everyone is gone here on the mountain. Nary a trace of my cabin. Cain't find my old hound, either. All I got is his teeth marks on my powder horn from when he was a puppy." His voice trailed off as he looked down the valley.

Finally, he stepped down beside me on the rock and said, "Stranger, I fully admire that puffed-up coat you're wearin'. Looks mighty warm. I never seen a color like that, either. Saw you from down in the valley and thought maybe a stump was on fire." He smiled but kept staring at me. "And that little rifle. Not much of a hole in the muzzle, is there? And you lost your ramrod, too. Maybe it's made for shootin' blue jays." He laughed and shook his head in wonderment.

Before I could defend my choice of deer hunting equipment, the blue jay left his perch and flew off to the top of a dead pine 60 yards below, where he resumed his raucous calls.

"Maybe I should clip off that branch he's setting on—but I hate to waste a bullet. Lead's mighty scarce since the war," my visitor said. "You can't find a good bullet these days."

Another reloader! I thought to myself.

"That's a mighty thin branch," I said skeptically.

114

"No smaller than the bullseye at Conroy's Crossing where we shoot for the beef. Best shots in the country toe the mark. You gotta be sharp to win one of those six quarters."

"Six? How can one beef be divided in six quarters?"

"Where you been, stranger? The fifth quarter is the hide and tallow, and the sixth is the lead that you dig out of the target and the tree . . . That was Ed's idea. The price is up to 20¢ a shot now, but we do have a fine old time."

"Who's the champion?" I asked.

"Depends. When George Rockwell, Miley Bull, Jerry Ehrens, and the likes of them master shots cut in, you gotta watch out. And now we've got them two big sailors that come up the Erie Canal from Carolina—Jack Monsell and Jim Lyons. Cain't hardly understand 'em but they sure can shoot. And if you can outwait Tom Nurnberger, the old Schuetzenfest champion, you might even take home a little tallow."

"What do you mean outwait Tom-what's-his-name?"

"Tom Nurnberger from Germany. A real block of granite. A slow and careful loader with powder, patch, and ball. He can hold that rifle on the targets for a coon's age—just waiting for the right second to touch her off . . . You heard what Dave Crosby said?"

"Nope, I don't believe I have."

"Well, when Tom came up to the mark last time, Dave said, 'Goodbye, boys.' 'Where you going, Dave?' we asked. 'Home to gather in my crops,' Dave said. 'But I'll be back before Tom Nurnberger shoots.' "

The blue jay, silent for a while, suddenly went back to his loud complaint at the very top of the dead pine.

"Can't do much around here with that," I said.

"Maybe I could," he said, as he slowly raised the long rifle, cocked the hammer, steadied his aim, and touched her off. A long, loud, low *whumpf* echoed down the valley as a cloud of white smoke blocked off our view. And when the smoke had slowly drifted away in the still air, the blue jay was gone, and the top of the dead pine just below his perch, a good 60 yards away, was neatly clipped. I turned to congratulate the stranger on his shot but he was gone. I looked around in amazement, and as I heard the far-off cry of our blue jay angrily protesting his eviction, I saw the stranger stop at the top of the trail, look back, and wave his rifle in farewell. Only then did I notice that he had left no tracks in the snow.

115

DO YOU REALLY WANT TO BE RESCUED?

SOMETHING that has always bothered me is the common belief—and I know you've heard it, too—that a drowning man sees his whole life flash before him. How you arrive at this assumption has often puzzled me. Did someone interview a man who was about to drown and had just been rescued? Did they ask him as he stood there dripping wet on the dock, "Excuse me, sir, but did your whole life flash before your eyes just before you grabbed that rope and they pulled you up here on the dock?" And did the man, who probably just wanted to go somewhere and lie down, answer, "Yes, it did. In a series of full-color instances that highlighted each specific phase of my existence." Or did he say, with water running off his nose, "Oh, shut up! I think I lost my car keys!"

I worry about such things. And I also worry about the role of the rescuer, who in too many situations goes unrecognized. Take the case of my friend and fellow hunter, Charlie Nash.

Charlie was a good guy and always willing to lend a hand to anyone in need. So one day when he was hunting desert quail in Arizona, a sudden flash flood marooned an old car full of frightened people in what had been a dry creek bed. Charlie went to their rescue in his Jeep. Hooking up his tow cable to the old car, he pulled them up out of the angry waters onto dry land. During the rescue, the bumper bracket of the old car came loose. On reaching the bank, the driver jumped out of his car and yelled, "Who is going to pay for my bumper?" According to Charlie, he seriously considered pushing him back into the creek.

Rescuing someone from a desert island is a constant ingredient of our literature dating back, I suppose, to Daniel

Defoe's *Robinson Crusoe*. But I wonder sometimes if the castaways always wanted to be rescued. "Let's get away from it all," and "out of the rat race" is the secret wish of many of us. But, speaking from experience, I can tell you that you can never get away from yourself—whether you're in downtown Cincinnati or the Fiji Islands.

Nevertheless, it's pleasant to contemplate an escape from a troubled world that seems to be speeding the wrong way down a one-way street. Like the sailor who had spent nearly three years on a deserted island, and one morning was elated to see a ship in the bay and a boat putting off to shore. As the boat grounded on the beach, an officer threw the sailor a bundle of current newspapers. "Compliments of the captain," said the officer. "He asks that you please read through these and then let us know if you still want to be rescued."

I suppose, in a sense, that we now live on a remote island here on Cape Hatteras, where it is said to be "about as far as you can go without getting close to someplace else." But the world is still with us and has become so busy, "getting and spending we lay waste our powers, little we see in nature that is ours." An Englishman named William Wordsworth said that a long time ago, but how true it is. Isn't it remarkable how busy we so-called "outdoors men" have become, and how few times a year in our hunting and fishing we actually take time to stop and look around us at the natural scenes and say, "Hey, man. This is ours."

So back to the rescue business. An old Connecticut friend, Pat Carroll, once had a grouse and deer hunting camp up in the backwoods of Maine. High on a wooded hill, it was also a quiet retreat to get away from it all. On this particular spring day Pat had taken the once-a-day train to the small town near his camp to spend a little time up on the hill. Throwing his duffle bag in the back of Nick Fingelly's wagon, they started for camp. After a long, hard winter, spring had finally come in all its glory to the Maine woods. The streams and rivers were bank high. As they made their way along the river road, the woods were so beautiful that Pat finally asked Nick to stop the wagon in order to walk it alone, while Nick took his bag up the hill to camp.

Crossing the bridge over the dark and swirling Pine River, Pat saw a little boy playing along the snow-covered bank. As he watched, Pat was horrified to see the boy suddenly slip off the bank and into the river. Whereupon Pat ran across 117 the bridge, vaulted over the snow bank, and, running down along the bank as the boy was being swept away, picked up a branch and thrust it out at the frightened youngster, who grabbed it tightly as Pat pulled him up on the bank. As they both stood there breathless, two local Maine men who had seen the incident from the bridge joined them and told Pat they would take care of the little boy. As Pat continued on his way, he suddenly realized how lucky it had been that he was there at just the right time to save a young life.

Arriving at his camp on the hill, Pat began to fix supper. The more he thought about the rescue, the better he felt. He had responded instantly and without fear. Not bad at all, he thought. Saving a life was not to be taken lightly. As Pat's self-esteem mounted, there was a knock at the door, and he opened it to find a man and woman standing on the porch.

"Good evening," the woman said. "Are you the man who pulled the little boy out of the river?"

"I am that man," Pat answered.

"Well, we're the little boy's parents, and we came up the hill to see you."

"That's certainly very nice of you," Pat said. "Won't you come in?"

"No," said the woman. "We can't come in. We just came up to ask you, did you happen to notice what's become of his mittens?"

35 I HAVEN'T SEEN YOU LATELY

"**H**EY, Ma," the little girl said as they drove along the country lane. "What's that scarecrow doing in the field with a gun?"

"Shh," her mother admonished. "That's your Uncle John. He's out hunting."

I well remember when a lot of us hunters could be mistaken for scarecrows with a gun. Seems like you found it only sensible to wear your oldest clothes when you had to fight the briars, brambles, and mud. In my case it was brown, baggy, button-up coveralls with a leather belt to hold you together in the middle, plus an old, ragged, canvas hunting coat somebody had left in the barn. And if you could afford one, an official, visored hunting cap with fuzzy-lined earflaps. The cap was important—it said you were a hunter, no doubt about it. But the rest of your uniform could be casual. Much like the clothes an ordinary scarecrow would wear.

But times have changed, and it's no longer proper, sensible, or even comfortable to look like a one-gallus possum hunter or a backwoods moonshiner when you take to the field. With the advent of amazing new materials, and the development of a layering system (we always did know that two light sweaters were warmer than one heavy one) there's no reason you can't keep warm and dry without looking and feeling like a two-legged, overstuffed sofa. Many is the time I've sat in an icy duck blind after putting on just one more jacket and wondered if I could get my gun up if a lonely duck flew by—and I usually couldn't. No more of that now with waterfowl parkas made of miraculous stuff called Cordura, Gore-Tex, and insulated with Thermolite. You stay warm, dry, and loose.

119

And as for those thick long johns we thought were standard underwear, we've come a long way, hunters, a long way. "Wickability." Sounds illegal, but it's the quality of modern polypropylene underwear that "wicks" away perspiration from the skin and allows it to dry quickly. And again you keep warm, dry, and happy.

And speaking to some of you older birds, do you remember when we certainly could have used some of that wickability? How about the time we tackled half a mile of a deep ditch full of thick, dusty, head-high horseweeds, trying to stomp out a cock pheasant or two? With our 22-pound shotgun at port arms, we fought and thrashed our way through that endless wall of weeds, and all on a nice, sunny October day. When we finally reached the end of the ditch, climbed up on that country road, and took off our lined, winter-weight, hunting cap, we stood there breathless with our hair stuck to our head. With sweat running off the end of our sunburned nose and down the middle of our back under those heavy long johns, we could have used a lot of wickability. But when we held up that nice, fat rooster, a cool breeze suddenly blew off the prairie and we were ready for another ditch.

For years a lot of us hunters have been wandering around in the woods and fields of America totally without camouflage. But no more of that. The desire not to be seen has taken over. Not only are there completely camouflaged hunting outfits, but now there are camouflaged swimsuits, Jeeps, bicycles, T-shirts, and coffee cups. Just the other day I saw an easy-to-see lady with a camouflaged purse. I hesitate to tell my wife, Ruby, of this threat. Her purse is hard enough to find here in the house without being camouflaged.

My young friend, Ryan Langowski, an energetic seven-year-old, is into the fad and often turns up in church in his camouflage outfit. "Dresses himself," his mother, Marta, says with a sigh. Then we play the game.

"Has anyone here seen Ryan Langowski? He seems to have disappeared."

"Here I am!" pipes up Ryan.

"I hear his voice," we say, "but I can't see him. Oh, there you are. You're camouflaged!"

"Yup," says Ryan with a happy grin.

But don't think you can just up and order a camouflaged hunting outfit. I've been studying the catalogs, and you have to carefully consider the exact kind of background into which you wish to disappear. Imagine your embarrassment if you have just dressed up in a RealTree camo shirt and four-pocket camo jeans and then, stumbling out of the woods, you suddenly find yourself in a cornfield. There you are, gun in hand, disguised as a tree—in a cornfield. With no time to change into a "cornstalk" camo outfit (also available) you can only stand stock-still, imitating a lone tree, and hope that the crows won't roost on your RealTree hat or a squirrel won't run up your leg.

You can now choose from a dozen camouflage hunting outfits each with a different pattern of deception. But be careful. If you start out in a "bottomland" camo rig and then somehow wander up into higher territory that calls for a "high country" camo outfit, you probably won't even get a shot. What's more, your dog may realize your blunder, give up in disgust, and head for home.

But, seriously, what's more reading fun than studying the artful, beautifully illustrated, outdoor equipment catalogs and seeing what has recently sprouted up in the fertile fields of mail-order merchandise? Well do I remember discovering L.L. Bean, Freeport, Maine, in the days when Mr. Bean wrote his own catalog advertising copy. To me his every word was straight from the forest, straight from the stream. Even to the caption below a plain, white cotton dress shirt. "The kind of shirt that Mr. Bean wears to and from the fishing camp," it said. I was about to send in my carefully saved $2.95 when my mother pointed out that I had exactly the same kind of shirts hanging in my closet. So Mr. Bean went on wearing his white shirt to and from the fishing camp, and I went on wearing my white shirt to and from the public school.

With all my recent interest in keeping these old hunting bones safe from the cold and wet, I was delighted to see that my former employer these many years, Remington Arms, has joined with DuPont and all their marvelous fibers and fabrics to produce a line of outdoor clothing and accessories designed by folks who hunt and fish. So, if you see an old guy in a new Remington hunting outfit this fall, looking warm, dry, and happy, look again. It may be me.

36 THINGS AIN'T ALWAYS WHAT THEY SEEM TO BE

L IKE most of my generation, I was raised on that most durable of myths, the everlasting, clean-living, clear-eyed, fast-shooting, hard-riding, western-movie cowboy. (But only "hard-riding" when he raced across the screen astride his faithful "hoss" in hoof-pounding pursuit of the bad guys, who galloped everywhere and were never good to their horses.) When he wasn't saving the ranch from the bad guys, he was bashfully wooing the rancher's daughter and being gentle and kind to his horse.

How could anyone forget William S. Hart, one of the early cowboy heroes. Out there on the sun-scorched Painted Desert, he slowly got off his exhausted but faithful horse, Thunder, took his canteen from the saddlebag, shook it sadly, and carefully shared his last, few, precious drops of water with Thunder. Then he *led* his horse across the desert in relentless pursuit of the "mangy coyotes" that had kidnapped the rancher's daughter.

I can still remember my embarrassment when William S. Hart and Thunder looked sorrowfully into the camera and my mother, who took me to the Saturday matinees when I was too young to go alone, leaned down to me in the dark and said in a whisper I knew that other kids could hear, "Isn't it amazing how much he looks like his horse?" And he did.

But, nevertheless, as a youngster I was determined to go west from Milwaukee, find a faithful horse out there on the range, and be good to it. Years later, when I had learned full well that movies and the real world are far apart, some of these adolescent dreams evidently still persisted.

We were coming down out of the Absaroka Mountains in 123

Montana after a successful 10-day elk hunt, and one of the good bulls on the trailing packhorses was mine. Rocking along in the creaking saddle with the beautiful Yellowstone Valley spread down before us, I thought how lucky I had been to draw a good horse. Buck was his name—a big, buckskin gelding. Surefooted, sensible, and comfortable, he was a pleasure to ride in spite of his saddle cinch in the morning. Tim, the wrangler, always came along, deflated him with a hard jab in the ribs, and then, with a strong heave, pulled the cinch up tight. "He's full of tricks, this horse. Just watch him," Tim would say.

But no need to warn me about this horse. Buck was my friend. I might even write a book about him called "Buck and Me" or "Good Luck Buck" or something. And then when we were about a mile above the ranch, Buck suddenly went lame. Right forefoot. I got off immediately, and by leaning into his shoulder and lifting on his fetlock, I finally wrestled up his big hoof. Tim and I then carefully checked his hoof and shoe. No lodged stone, no loose shoe, but still a limp.

"I think he just got tired of carrying you, Jack. He does that," Tim said. "Get back on him and go easy."

Not me, I thought. This was *my* chance to show how a good cowboy treats his horse. It was "The Law of the Plains." So, much to Tim's amusement, I took the reins in hand and started to lead Buck down the rough and rocky mountain trail. As the rest of the pack train passed me, I was treated to such remarks as, "Whats a matter, Jack, out of gas?" "You shoulda checked your tires!" "Don't worry, we'll save you a beer . . . a small one." Very funny.

Cowboy boots are made for riding, not walking, and by the time we reached the ranch and the corral, we both were limping. Leading Buck up to a corral rail, I undid the cinch, pulled the blanket and saddle off his sweaty back, and, with a grunt, heaved them up on the rail. Old Buck shook himself with relief and dropped his head for me to unbuckle his bridle. I slipped the bridle down over his ears, slid the bit out of his mouth, and turned away from good old Buck, my faithful companion of the high trails. Whereupon he reached over, bared his big yellow teeth, and bit me so hard on the top of my shoulder that I yelled out loud in pain and surprise, swung the bridle around, and slapped him hard across the nose. With this, he snorted, swung away from me, and, with

124

tail high, trotted happily off to join the other horses—with nary a limp.

My loud yell brought my companions out of the bunkhouse, where they had been celebrating a successful hunt (without waiting for me, of course). They came up to the rail, cold refreshments in hand, and asked in chorus, "What happened?" And when I said, still rubbing my shoulder, in a loud and outraged voice, "The so and so *bit* me!" they all gave a disgusting enactment of vulgar and unwarranted merriment, hanging onto each other and whooping and yelling with laughter. So much for "The Law of the Plains."

After a winter of carefully planning a Montana elk hunt and a summer of happy expectation, it's a real letdown to arrive promptly on the fall scene only to find that your big game guide and outfitter has left town. "Heard he's gone down to Idaho somewhere," they tell you.

That's what happened to a friend of mine, Bill Adams, and he's still talking about it. With no guide in sight and nothing else to do, Bill and his partner went to the local bar in town, where they met John. "Looked like he was just out of the movies," Bill said. "Quiet, reserved, steel-gray hair, face all wrinkled and weathered, beat up old Stetson. And equally impressive when he talked elk hunting. When we told him about our predicament, we were delighted to hear him offer us his services. A real mountain-wise elk hunting guide with his own outfit.

"So off we went at daybreak the next morning. A *long*, hard ride—almost sawed me in half. Way to hell and gone up in the Absarokas. Finally made camp just at dark. Up early the next morning, eager to go. And when we asked, 'Okay, John, where do we hunt today?' our trusty old guide said, 'Beats me. I ain't never been back this far before.' "

If these two tales have a moral, we might borrow from the infinite wisdom of the world's greatest philosophers and profound thinkers, who have said: "Sorry, kid. But things ain't always what they seem to be!"

BREATHLESS ON MY BACK AT 16,000 FEET

37

"**B**REATHLESS on my back at 16,000 feet behind a granite ledge in the lofty peaks of the Bookasaupuka Mountains, I wondered if the band of Marco Polo sheep, led by the gigantic ram who had to be the granddaddy of all wild sheep in the world, had spotted me and Mahdu, my loyal, wiry, and turbaned guide. Mahdu shared my excitement but not my breathlessness as he peeked cautiously and slowly over the ledge and then turned to me with an eager smile that creased his brown, wrinkled face. They were still there. As I waited to catch my breath for that one long, crucial shot, I suddenly wondered what string of amazing events had put me in remote and forbidden Hellandgoneaya, high on the roof of the world."

Sound familiar? It ought to. It's the standard formula for starting almost every hunting story you have read in the last 20 years. Plunge right in. Get to the point. Don't waste a lot of words and time fooling around with the tiresome details of how you got there. Start at the top. But I actually remember when most of the "bait and bullet" writers used to start a story where it began—at the beginning.

Remember when it went something like this: "I was just having my second cup of coffee, sitting at the kitchen table, when I heard Joe's old car (you never went hunting in a *new* car) rattle to a stop at the curb. It was opening day of the narwhal season, and our preparations had been mighty. Old Bowser heard Joe's car, too, went to the door, and whined. Looking back at me he seemed to know that a day afield with his boss lay ahead, and he was ready to go. Opening the door, I yelled out to Joe, 'Come on in, you old poacher. Coffee's on the stove.' "

Remember that? And then the story of the hunt went on logically and in proper order until you closed with old Bowser lying in front of the fireplace all tuckered out—narwhals are hard to retrieve—while you and Joe analyzed and relived each shot of the day and made plans for a future hunt.

You wouldn't have much of a chance selling a story like that today—except for possibly the narwhal angle and if you had some good photos (not like my "action" shots, which often turn out to be tack-sharp close-ups of my own thumb!). Or if that particular narwhal you were hunting was a dangerous menace that had speared some friendly natives lately.

Friendly natives and native guides always make good copy—particularly if they are turbaned like Mahdu, the native sheep hunting guide at 16,000 feet. And speaking of turbans, I heard one in County Kerry last spring about the Irishman who, on his first trip to London, was shown a great kindness by a turban-wearing Pakistani bus conductor. As he stepped off the bus, he said, "Thank you very much, sir, and I hope your head gets better soon!"

But someday, somehow I hope to have a loyal, wilderness-wise, turbaned guide. The last guide I had wore a cap that said "Agway Fertilizers" and got lost twice.

Have you noticed, too, that although most of us have never been charged by an infuriated rhino, treed by a marauding grizzly, stalked by a killer lion, trampled by a rogue elephant, or even sprung upon by the usual run-of-the-mill, man-eating leopard, we certainly like to read about such adventures? That's why I've often wondered if maybe I shouldn't try to get a little more action, suspense, and high adventure with dangerous game into the kind of hunting I usually write about. Take, for example, the average, old-fashioned rabbit hunt with the baying of beagles breaking the silence of snow-covered swamps locked in the grip of winter. Away we go again, chasing those harmless rabbits.

No more of that. How about this approach: "It was cold, and I hadn't felt my toes since an hour ago. Rifle in hands, I stamped my boots on the top of the big cedar stump and waited for a possible charge by 'Old Long Tooth,' the killer rabbit of Baranowski's Bog. How had I found myself in this dangerous predicament, about to face one of the fiercest rabbits that had ever savaged this once-peaceful countryside? I was beginning to wonder if maybe I shouldn't go back to my car, drive home, and go back to bed. Old Long Tooth 127 had actually driven entire packs of bleeding and torn hounds, whining and shivering with tail between their legs, back to the trucks of their amazed owners.

"This madness among attacking, squealing rabbits under the leadership of Old Long Tooth had spread to such an extent that schools had been closed, factories and stores shut down, and doors barricaded until only the bravest of men had formed the 'Rabbit Rangers' to fight this menace of renegade rabbits. Young and telling myself I was always in for adventure, I had applied for an opening in the Rangers. I had undergone intensive training in rabbit punching, cold tracking, and burrow digging. Now I was about to be tested. This was the day I would win my 'Ears'—or be rabbit-kicked, pummeled, and ripped beyond all recognition. . . ."

On the other hand, I might just recognize that nothing ever stays the same in hunting—or writing about it—and become one of the first vigilant stalwarts to warn you of what the Age of Electronics might do to hunting. For quite a while now I have been objecting to what electronics has done to some phases of so-called "sport fishing." Fishing used to be a lazy, contemplative, philosophical pastime designed to do just that—*pass the time* for people who wanted to be lazy and relax for a while, peacefully contemplating that cork-bobber and smiling philosophically when a dragonfly tried to light on it. Huckleberry Finn, Old Man River style. I wonder what Huck would think today if a fleet of chrome-trimmed, tournament bass boats, bristling with fish-finders, went roaring up his river accompanied by the sounds of blasting stereos, electric, snarlproof reels, and the frenzied antics of the occupants in upholstered swivel chairs trying to catch more fish than the other guy? I wonder? But do you know how many people have listened to my objections? You guessed it. Nobody!

So, now, don't say I didn't warn you about the new, electronic, single-chip radar system that has been developed by Texas Instruments, Inc. A single radar chip made from gallium arsenide and operating at 10 gigahertz can be easily inserted into the stock of your gun. Portable game-finding radar. Obviously we must now get ready for a new deer hunting alibi: "There I was, operating my radar with all the quiet woodland skill I could muster, when a blip of the biggest buck I'd ever scoped came on the screen. And wouldn't you know it—one of my gigahertz fell off!"

38 CHRISTMAS TREES AND RASPBERRIES

AS a hunter gets older, the hills get steeper, the deer look much farther away, and that old rifle scope seems to fuzz up just when you need it the most. The lenses are probably worn out after all those years of looking through them.

In fact, a lot of things seem to fuzz up at the edges, but I've noticed that a happy family time like Christmas brings back memories loud and clear—in sharp focus and full color. All it takes is the smell of a fresh-cut balsam tree in the house and I'm a kid again, back in the corner behind the family Christmas tree reading my new book, *Bobby Blake at Snowtop Camp*, by the warm glow of the colored tree lights.

As some of you Bobby Blake readers may recall, Bobby had just received a brand new .22 rifle for Christmas (much to my envy because I had yet to get my own gun), and I followed each page with mounting interest. Shortly after giving Bobby this great gift, the Blake family went off for the holidays to Snowtop Camp, high in the faraway, snow-covered mountains.

And then came the big scene. Betsy Blake, Bobby's little sister, for some reason or another is walking along a narrow trail on the side of a snow-covered cliff when suddenly Bobby, who is in the valley below with bearded Old Dan, sees the sinuous shape of a stalking cougar on Betsy's trail. "Shoot at once, old friend Dan," Bobby yells.

"I can't, my rifle is jammed with snow. It's your shot, Bobby. Aim true," Dan yelled back.

129

Well, you know how that turned out. One shot from Bobby's new rifle—right between the cougar's eyes—and Betsy is saved from tooth and claw.

The reason I remember all this so well is that years later I borrowed the same scene for a cartoon-style Remington advertisement. Same trail, same cougar, same little girl; except with a few added commercial overtones. I had written: "Bob, take your Remington Model 512 rifle loaded with those hardhitting Kleanbore .22s and nail that cougar," Dan yelled. You can image how surprised I was to later read that same line of copy in a short bit entitled "Yells We Doubt Were Ever Yelled" in the sophisticated *The New Yorker* magazine. Oh well, it isn't every writer that gets his work reviewed in *The New Yorker*.

A lot of Christmas days at my grandparents Mitchell come back clearly this time of year, and I can still see the spectacular tree in the parlor literally ablaze with brightly burning, *real* 131 wax candles. Obviously a hazardous display because there was a big tin bucket of water at the foot of the tree for an emergency dousing if necessary. You have never really seen a lighted Christmas tree with its ornaments gleaming and shimmering in the early dark of Christmas morn until you've seen a tree that is truly candle lit.

Once you entered the old, faded brick Mitchell house, there was no doubt about the interests of its male occupants. It was full of taxidermists' art and trophies of the chase. I well remember one that would probably raise the hackles of a protectionist. It was a full-feathered, sandhill crane made into a long-legged lamp with a naked lightbulb dangling from its beak. It was the only sandhill crane that Granddad ever shot, and my grandmother usually pushed it way back into a dark corner where it seemed to be continually searching for a frog.

Christmas at the senior Mitchell's house was, of course, marked by a gigantic, belt-busting family dinner built around the glory of a huge, farm-raised Wisconsin turkey stuffed with an oyster and wild rice dressing. There might have been a few tokens of the hunt such as a side dish of roast duck or a platter of grouse, but the main event was that giant, plump turkey. The oysters that went into Grandma's special stuffing were kept in a wooden box at the foot of the cellar stairs where it was cold, dark, and damp. And we kids would open the door in the kitchen, peer down the steep stairs, and listen to the oysters. Since then, I have checked with some prominent bivalve experts on the possibility of listening to oysters and have received some pretty strange looks. But, we *did* hear them. And besides, Milwaukee is a long way from the Chesapeake Bay.

Grandma's wild raspberry preserves were always served with the turkey, and I well remember Granddad with the bowl in his hand looking sternly, but with a twinkle in his eye, down the table at my cousin, Red Cummings, and me as he said, "I hope that there are no leaves in these raspberries."

"No, sir," we both said as we grinned and squirmed a little. The leaves in the raspberries had happened the summer before on a family raspberry picking trip up north on the Peshtigo River. Red and I had made the mistake of substituting a layer of leaves in the bottom of our berry pails to speed up the filling so that we could be excused to go trout fishing.

The substitution was immediately discovered by our elders, and I remember a few hard whacks on the rear. Our fishing rods went back in the truck, and we started all over again to fill up those everlasting, enormous tin lard pails—one berry at a time—as the trout stream sang enticingly over the rocks. And we never did fill our buckets in time to go fishing.

After dinner was over and the ladies and the smaller children had adjourned to the kitchen and the back parlor, the fully stuffed men moved to the front parlor to taper off on apples and a big bowl of nuts. My father, three uncles, and my grandfather in his high-backed chair were about to hold the regular family meeting on hunting and fishing. Red and I sat quietly on the floor near the tree, supposedly puzzling over the intricacies of our meccano sets but really making believe that we were part of the meeting. After enough apples had been crunched and enough walnuts cracked, the men got down to serious business.

"Dad," one of the sons would finally say, "we've been discussing a possible change on the marsh."

"Is that so?" Granddad would reply, looking calmly around the room.

"Yes, sir," the spokesman would say. "We think we should move the point blind about 80 yards in toward Canvasback Bay."

Granddad would then lean back in his judicial chair, stare at the ceiling for a while, and finally say, "Well, let's discuss it."

And discuss it they would. All the pros and cons of where the wind might blow and the ducks might fly while Red and I listened intently to every word because we knew full well that some windy, fall morning we, too, would be sitting in that blind on Canvasback Bay.

IF TODAY WAS A FISH I'D THROW IT BACK

39

I ONCE heard a folk song that will describe my present predicament. The title was "If Today Was a Fish I'd Throw It Back."

It all started early this morning with the complete breakdown of my new office filing system. At my wife's suggestion (all right then, my wife's *insistence*) I have set up this modern, highly organized, and alphabetized set of file drawers with folders, colored tabs, and separators. It was originally planned for four drawers, but since the cat likes to sleep in the lower one, loudly protesting when removed, we are using only three drawers at the present time.

Having spent far too much of my life in an office (before the computer) I am completely familiar with the complexity of a filing system and have been known to actually locate, use, and return a filed item to its proper place under the watchful eye of a politely smiling lady. But, as I now realize, someone else did the original filing.

Constantly wracked and torn by decisions, I can't seem to get the hang of it. Take this shotgun rubber recoil pad, for example. No sooner had I brought it home from Bryan Perry's Frisco Rod and Gun Shop here on the Outer Banks than Ruby said, "Now, remember where you put it." No problem, I thought. I'll *file* it away for installation at a later date. But where? Under "R" for rubber or "RR" for rubber recoil? Or "P" for pad—and that was too close to a folder marked

"Partridge." I removed it, sat back down, and found myself rereading William Harnden Foster's memorable dedication of his great book, *New England Grouse Shooting,* to his and my good friend, Bill, Jr., ". . . who hunted with me the pa'tridge covers that his great grandfather hunted years before I was born." After a few sighs for the past, I questioned the *placement* of the folder in the file. Should it be under pa'tridge, partridge, or grouse? See what I mean?

Still searching for the right file for "recoil pad," I considered "Accessories" in the top drawer, which seemed logical enough, but again my interest strayed to the folder "Accumulated" (story ideas), which suddenly reminded me of my November deadline for this Page. So I opened the folder containing only one single, skinny page of my hasty scribbles.

Now, at best, my handwriting wins no prizes. My valued friend and aide, Finn Hoff, who lives just across the canal and types all this stuff, will heartily agree. As a scholar, Finn speaks four languages and occasionally accuses me of making up one of my own. Maybe that's why I just received a sporting goods catalog, which I had "handwritten" away for, addressed to "Jack D. Nutshell."

Realizing that I really had to get going on this "Back Page," I put the recoil pad on the window sill where it will remain until Ruby "neatens up"—then never to be seen again. With that I started to decipher my story notes, but everything had either been used or I couldn't quite figure out what I had meant in the first place.

Now, I know full well that somewhere in these drawers is another file folder bursting with story ideas, each one a unique and original key to literary greatness, but I can't find it. Fortunately, I finally turned to "Miscellaneous," one of my broadest file categories. (In fact, it takes up nearly all of Drawer No. 2.) And there before my very eyes was a fairly recent report from an old friend, Dr. Joseph P. Linduska, who, after a long and illustrious worldwide career in wildlife conservation, has retired to Chestertown on the Eastern Shore of Maryland with all its hunting and fishing.

Since Joe and I have always seemed to share a view of a world that is rarely what it seems to be, he brought me up to date on his recent struggles with a newly acquired, highly portable hunting and fishing boat. "Comes in a package four inches thick, two feet wide and can be assembled, it says, by one man in one minute into a twelve-foot boat—just right

135

for my 7½ h.p. outboard motor." I had already begun to grin when I started Joe's account of how he and his neighbor (a *licensed* engineer, Joe points out) finally got the boat unfolded and assembled in a mere 35 minutes, but I laughed out loud at his final line: ". . . after having got *trapped* inside it two or three times!" I can just see Lillian, Joe's wife, watching all this with her usual amused and quiet tolerance.

Like I've been taught, I was neatly returning the folders to the file, and while putting back the "Partridge" folder under the Ps and right near one marked "Pig Pickin" (the subject of September's "Back Page") I looked to see what I had forgotten to put in the story. Sure enough, there was a scribbled but readable note made way back on September 1, 1984, on the Blalock's front porch while waiting for the 34th pig to come brown and crispy out of George Smith's stainless steel barbeque oven, ready for the "pig pickin" and just before the big dove hunt. The subject somehow was "atheism," which I can assure you is not a popular position in Plymouth, N.C. It was then that young Gregg Spencer spoke up and said, "There are no *scared* atheists."

Seems he was a mate on an offshore charter fishing boat appropriately named *The Deep Water*."We were well off-shore, with only me working on the rear deck and the captain up on the bridge. No one else aboard. That's when a railing collapsed and overboard I went. And the boat went on, leaving me all by myself in the ocean, 25 miles out to sea. Nobody heard my yells but somebody sure heard my prayers because the captain suddenly turned around and saw me far astern. When he came back to pick me up he said, surprised-like, 'What in the world are you doing out there?' Like it was my idea!" And we all laughed with Gregg. Suddenly it was quiet . . . and for a fleeting moment each one of us was adrift, alone in the awesome sea.

When my new filing system becomes completely operative with all my story ideas neatly and properly pigeon-holed and classified, we can all look forward to better organization of this Page. On the other hand, it may well be like the man who visited his doctor to complain, "I can't seem to stick to one subject for more than a minute, Doc. My mind just jumps all around!"

"How long have you had this trouble?" the Doctor asked.

"What trouble?" the man answered.

So bear with me, friends, bear with me.

40 LET ME TELL YOU JUST HOW IT HAPPENED

HAVE you heard about the old, gray hunter who showed up one day at his church's confessional booth? In a low and tremulous voice he told the waiting priest, "I'm 89 years old and I'm here to tell you that last Saturday my grandsons and one great-grandson took me out for what they probably figured was my last deer hunt. To get me out of the way, I think, they put me high up on my old deer stand on Anderson Hill, overlooking Plum Valley. Rough going up from the jeep trail with my arthritis and all, but with a lot of puffing and pushing they got me located, all wrapped up in a blanket, sitting up against that big pine. They handed me my cane, my old rifle, and a thermos of coffee and took off. *It was colder than the hinges of* . . . Excuse me, Father, it was *very* cold, but I've been cold before. And when they came back to pick me up, there I was with a big 10-point buck. One shot, 180 yards. My great-grandson, Johnny, paced it off with a whoop and a holler on every step."

"Well, that's just fine," the priest said, "but evidently you didn't have a license or a deer tag or something."

"Nope," was the answer, "everything was legal. License, tag, everything."

"Then why are you telling me all this here at confession?"

The old hunter said proudly, "Because I'm telling *everybody!*"

And that's the way it goes. When you've got news of that importance, don't bottle it up. Let the world know.

But it isn't always easy to get someone's complete attention so you can tell them every important detail of just how you made the shot. Do you ever get the feeling that their friendly

137

smile is becoming a little frozen, or that they are staring at your right ear or looking around for the nearest exit? That's why you have to be constantly alert for opportunities to tell your story. Like the westerner who said, "With this lull in conversation, do you mind if I say a few words about Texas?" Or pushing it even further with the interruption, "Speaking of the federal deficit, have I told you about the double I made on ruffed grouse?"

One important tip to consider is your reputation for sticking somewhere near the truth. This simple fact can have a lot to do with the reception you can expect when you tell your hunting story. In that great book *On the Road with Charles Kuralt*, I read about a farmer in North Carolina whose reputation for ignoring the truth was so bad that he had to get a neighbor to call his cows. So watch out for such items as measurement, weights, distances from the muzzle, horn size, etc. Work as much truth into the story and people may listen.

I never had much luck convincing anyone that I have made some very unusual and highly spectacular shots in my time. The skepticism of my listeners may be due to their having once been a witness to my shooting on a very bad day, when my hunting coat was buttoned up wrong, or when I had forgotten to wear my lucky shoelaces. One of those days when, after firing a full magazine of shells at a flock of ducks close enough to knock off your hat and not a feather is ruffled, you hold your gun at arm's length and wonder how far you could throw it back in the marsh with one good swing!

That is probably why I have so much trouble with my absolutely true story of "four ducks at 40 yards with one shot." Granted this is quite a claim, but it nevertheless did happen.

The gun, I should explain, was my dad's Parker 10-gauge magnum double, weighing a mere 12 pounds and loaded with two ounces of No. 4 shot in a 3½-inch shell. And what's more, it was the first shot I had ever fired with this venerable cannon.

The ducks were shovelers, and the place was Blue Dog Lake, Waubay, South Dakota, and the date was a long time ago, about the fall of 1940. On that memorable day, a big flock of shovelers (you may call them spoonbills) came high over the pass between Blue Dog and Redhead Slough. I led